OFF THE

CAPES OF DELAWARE

This book IS PUBLISHED
FROM THE PROCEEDS OF
THE LUDWIG VOGELSTEIN
MEMORIAL FUND

BENJAMIN W. BLANDFORD

OFF THE
CAPES OF DELAWARE

Tales of American Jewish Pioneers and Patriots

ILLUSTRATIONS BY BERNARD SEGAL

UNION OF AMERICAN HEBREW
CONGREGATIONS · *New York* · MCMXL

For some time the Union of American Hebrew Congregations has been engaged in preparing and publishing new books to meet the needs of pupils in the high school department of our religious schools, of young people in our youth groups, and of adults in their adult study circles or colleges of Jewish studies. But a well rounded Jewish education includes not only the formal study of Jewish history and literature, the religion, the customs and institutions of Judaism and the Hebrew language, Jewish current events and music; it provides also for the enjoyment of Jewish leisure reading. And for this purpose a special literature, less formal in character, has to be prepared. A significant area to be explored in this connection is that of American Jewish history. All of us should, especially in these days, be interested in the stories of Jewish participation in the upbuilding of America. In writing a series of stories of American Jewish life—the first, as far as I know, intended for people above the elementary school age—Mr. Blandford has rendered Jewish education a genuine service.

But this work is unique for another reason: Mr.

Blandford is a non-Jew. And many years ago the thought came to him that it is both wise and necessary to look at American history in terms of the commonly shared activities in which Jew and gentile engaged in pioneer days, when they worked side by side to help build our great country. Absolute historic accuracy in every detail is not claimed by the author for these stories. However, his fiction is woven on the loom of fact, and he engaged in much careful and painstaking research of the sources to give his stories authentic historical background.

His book, we believe, shows the indomitable pioneering spirit of some of the sons and the daughters of Israel as they participated in the founding and in furthering the growth of America. These courageous men and women actually lived, labored, loved, fought their battle of life, wrestled with and solved their problems, and passed on, leaving to posterity their good names and memories. So truly democratic were these Jewish pioneers in America that only the bare outlines of their heroic lives are recorded. Mr. Blandford engages in a labor of love when he waves the magic wand of fiction and causes them to live again for the glory of Israel and for the encouragement of Jewry of today.

EMANUEL GAMORAN

Upon the shelves of our great libraries, half forgotten and already yellowing with age and gathering dust, lie the laborious efforts of our great and conscientious research workers. Volumes which tell the history of the struggles of pioneer Americans—both Jew and gentile—and of their lives and loves, their failures and their successes. Seldom are these books taken down and studied. In this rush-a-day world few have the time or inclination to do so. But, significant in these days when temporary dictatorial upstarts arise and tell us that only one class or one group of certain beliefs, or blood, or what-not, are the only true-blue patriots, is the fact that in America all classes, of all religious, social, and racial stocks co-operated to give us our America.

Jew and gentile struggled and intertwined together, one with the other, and in their revolutions and evolutions created that strongly interlaced rope called "Democracy" that binds us all—Jew and gentile, Catholic and Protestant—one to another, and will prevent our nation from falling into that whirlpool of hate, intolerance, and cruelty into which other nations are today plunging.

The author, through these stories, has sought to bring to life from the quiet shelves in dark corners of our libraries, the men and women of all classes in the historic past and show what they thought and said, and what they did and died for, but particularly to impress on the reader's mind that Jew cooperated with gentile, and gentile with Jew to the glory of a triumphant democracy.

B. W. B.

ACKNOWLEDGMENT OF THANKS

In connection with the collating of material for these historic sketches of Jewish life in North America, the author acknowledges a debt of gratitude to Mr. Albert M. Friedenberg, Dr. George Alexander Kohut, Mr. Max J. Kohler, Mr. Leon Hühner, and other indefatigable research workers and members of the American Jewish Historical Society; and to the editors of *The American Hebrew* Magazine in whose pages these stories originally appeared. To Dr. David Philipson, Rabbi George Zepin, and to Dr. Emanuel Gamoran, of the Union of American Hebrew Congregations, for their kind assistance and co-operation, the author feels deeply grateful and appreciative. And to my genial friend, Mr. Walter Hart Blumenthal who first suggested these stories as an opening door to a better understanding between Jew and gentile, I hereby dedicate this book in loving respect.

THE AUTHOR

CONTENTS

CONTENTS

ILLUSTRATIONS

OFF THE

CAPES OF DELAWARE

THE storm had passed and the brig *Priscilla*, dismasted, lay becalmed off the Delaware Capes on a sultry day in August, 1768.

"This voyage has brought nothing but bad luck," muttered Abraham Isaacs, owner and captain, throwing down the cards with a gesture of disgust and accepting the proffered wine-bottle from John Merritt, his mate, a much younger man.

"Come, Cap'n," replied his companion. "Don't talk so gloomily. See yon dark line? 'Tis the Delaware country. Our boats could reach it, but there's naught there in Zwaanendael, that great valley of wild swans, so let's play. Here, deal the cards, while we wait for a passing vessel to aid us in rigging up a jury-mast."

"I can gamble no more," growled Isaacs. "You've taken my last shekel."

"The pearls you told me of," suggested Merritt,

3

glancing out to sea through narrowed eyelids as though to hide the cunning in his eyes.

"The pearls I dare not wager," replied the Jew, nervously stroking the thin white hairs on his chin. "They're family heirlooms and belong to my wife."

"Just one bead," pleaded the other. "You said each pearl was worth a small fortune in itself."

"Curse you, no!" shouted the Jew angrily.

"Very well, then," Merritt replied, laying down the cards. "Abraham Isaacs, who has faced many an adventure and has never returned home empty-handed, has at last lost, and Newport will say ——"

"Stop!" thundered the Jew. "I will wager ——"

"A pearl bead?" interrupted Merritt, bending forward eagerly.

"No!" Abraham replied after a moment's pause. "Not a bead, but this brig!"

"This wreck, you mean!" exclaimed Merritt.

"But she is good and stout. Remasted and repaired at Matthias Bush's shipyard at Wilmington, her worth will then be the same as when she left Newport Harbor."

"That was fifteen hundred dollars," mused Merritt.

"Fifteen hundred dollars"—Captain Abraham Isaacs was writing it on a scrap of paper. "Here, son," he cried to a young man who was reading in the shade of a sail stretched from the broken mast, "be witness to this."

"Father, please don't gamble," begged young Jacob.

4

"Silence!" the old man ordered. " 'Tis not for you to question your elders. Sign!"

Jacob signed, and with a sigh turned away.

A few minutes later Abraham savagely kicked the cask he sat on, while Merritt, with beaming face and dancing eyes, for he was now owner of the brig, shouted: "I feel a breeze rising. Our luck is changing, Jew! If we could only get help!"

Abraham's thin face flushed at the unusual, insolent tone, while Jacob strode over and faced Merritt. "Speak not in that tone to my father!" he cried. "He raised you from cabin-boy to mate and has always treated you fair."

John Merritt snapped his fingers in derision. "Poor fool," he sneered. "Your honored father has gambled your birthright away. Now the brig is mine. I want not this wreck, however," he continued, "but its worth in gold."

"You won't get it," Jacob growled.

"There's no way to prevent me."

"Then I'll invent a way," the young Jew replied.

"Again our inventor dreams. Always inventing, always failing," laughed Merritt.

The threatened quarrel was averted by an excited sailor hastening to where Abraham, suddenly grown old and gray, sat with his face buried in his hands.

"The water-casks are empty, Cap'n," the man cried, touching his forelock respectfully. "The hot sun has sprung the staves and ——"

Instantly Captain Isaacs was alert. He sent a boat crew with a couple of casks toward the fast-receding land for a fresh supply. In the rising breeze the crippled ship was helplessly drifting away from the land.

Day by day, however, the brig was carried by the varying current first out into the broad Atlantic, then almost within sight of the Delaware Capes, while the weather continued hot, the sky cloudless. The crew were put on short rations with a daily allowance of a cupful of muddy water from the bottom of the broken casks. No other ships were sighted.

"What are you dreaming about, inventor?" queried Merritt of Jacob Isaacs, as, sitting on a coil of rope, he appeared immersed in deep thought. "The maids of Newport's Jewish colony?"

"No," replied Jacob, stung by the other's tone. "I was thinking—so much water around us, yet we suffer from thirst."

"Why don't you invent a magic bucket that would change the water from salt to fresh the moment a sailor hauled it from the sea?"

Jacob walked away to avoid the taunting voice, but he muttered to himself his oft repeated phrase, "I'll invent a way."

Abraham Isaacs rapidly weakened from the moment he lost his ship by gambling. Stricken with remorse, he often looked upon his son with fond though sad eyes. Then one evening, after a trying day of

6

stifling heat, he quietly fell asleep to awake no more on the troubled waters.

Day succeeded day. A sailor in delirium plunged into the sea, crying, "There's water! Let us drink!" The others grew weak and sick.

At last there were but few men left aside from Jacob Isaacs and John Merritt.

Jacob found that by moistening a rag in his meager allowance of water it lasted longer. But now, for two days, not a drop had passed their dry, cracking lips. All the while the sun poured down its radiant heat from out of a brazen sky, and although a fair breeze had wafted the ship into the waters of Delaware Bay, within sight of land, the men were far too weak to lower a boat.

Then Jacob made a discovery—he found a decanter of water in his father's cabin, the sun sparkling on its diamond facets! Beneath it a note in his father's handwriting. "Son, my atonement!" it said.

Realizing that his father had saved his daily allowance of water in order that his son might thereby hold on to life longer, Jacob, in his weakness, wept freely.

Turning, he saw John Merritt stretching out his hands piteously from the couch on which he had fallen in weakness. "Water!" the blackened lips pleaded.

Jacob's first impulse was to give him a cupful; then, remembering the gambling debt, he staggered over and whispered, "Merritt, listen! That gambling paper for a drink!"

Merritt, too weak to murmur, rolled over and hid his face. His action spoke refusal louder than any words.

"Then die! Curse you, die!" snarled Jacob. "You tricked and ruined your best friend, my father, and robbed me of my own. Die! Then I'll take that cursed paper from your rotting body before the sea claims you as its own." Jacob took a long, gurgling draught from the decanter.

Merritt groaned at the sound and feebly rolled over, revealing a face pallid with swiftly approaching death.

Jacob stopped suddenly, with decanter uplifted. The dying man unnerved him; his conscience was troubled. Then, "Here, devil take you, drink! I cannot let you perish! But I'll invent a way to circumvent your evil plotting."

They both drank deeply, then remembered no more; while the brig, broadside on, gently grounded on a sandy beach where a few hours later a party of Indian clam-diggers found the survivors.

Back in Newport, a heart-breaking situation faced Jacob Isaacs, for his beloved mother collapsed on hearing the sad news. Soon Jacob and Sarah, his young sister, were left alone in the world. To make matters worse, they were penniless. Even the valuable pearls had somehow disappeared, and careful search had not disclosed their whereabouts. John Merritt, too, had not failed to press his claim and had filed suit for fifteen hundred dollars "in gold" in payment of Abraham Isaacs' debt.

Then followed days of trial for Jacob, for, while the lower court ruled that the debt could be paid "in goods and chattels" from proceeds of the estate, the vindictive Merritt fought the case through the higher courts until Jacob appealed to the King in Council for final adjudication, and Merritt, much to his disgust, was definitely awarded the brig, slowly rotting away on the sandy shores of Delaware.

In the little seaport of Wilmington, in that part of the colony of Pennsylvania known as Delaware, lived Matthias Bush, the Jewish ship-owner. To him, as a business acquaintance of his father, Jacob went for advice and found in the bustling little business man with ever-smiling eyes a true friend who gave him employment, first in his brokerage department, then on his vessels until the Revolution drove merchant ships to the safety of the ports like flocks of frightened, white-winged sea-birds.

Then, when peace came, Jacob met Aaron Lazarus, a young Jew from South Carolina. Both men, being of inventive minds and kindred spirits, became bosom friends.

"If steam can be forced to turn those paddle-wheels," remarked Aaron one morning as they watched the newly invented steam-driven boat of

Ramsey and Fitch slowly puffing its way down the Delaware River, "I see no reason why horses could not be removed from coaches and steam-engines substituted, and if the wheels ran on iron tracks with a wagon-load of lumber attached, one might go from Wilmington to Philadelphia, yea, even to New York, quicker and smoother than in our finest coaches."

"Perhaps," agreed Jacob. "Why not experiment?"

"I have," quietly replied Aaron. "I made a model engine, but the expense—" he stopped significantly.

"Why not experiment with it on one of these little sloops? They lie idle since the war, waiting for trade to return to our shores. I am sure Master Matthias will give us permission. I'll ask him today," concluded Jacob enthusiastically.

Matthias Bush readily gave assent and soon from the center of one of the smaller sloops a high, turtle-back boiler appeared, and the noise of hammering and pipe-fitting resounded from the little covered wharf by the river front.

"This river muck clogs up the pipes," remarked Aaron disgustedly, looking up from the iron door of the little furnace. His face was smeared with oil and grease, his hands dirty with ill-smelling mud. "How can it be overcome?"

"Let's cease using the river water and since we must not tap the village drinking water, let's row to the Delaware Capes with a barrel and bring back clear sea water."

Suiting the action to the words, the young men and Jacob's sister Sarah, who came "to help with the oars," she said, much to the secret joy of Aaron, rowed out to the open sea and filled the barrel.

Returning to Matthias Bush's dock, they rolled it to the little ship and emptied it into the boiler. The fire was started, and although steam was made, there was no force, only a disappointing trickle of sparkling water from the tips of the cylinders.

Aaron's face took on a look of disappointment. " 'Tis the same as usual. A failure!" he remarked.

"Too many pipes, perhaps," suggested Jacob. He idly placed his hand, moistened by the dripping cylinders, to his mouth. To his surprise, the salt was gone! It tasted sweet and refreshing.

His look of bewilderment gave place to a few moments of deep thought. Then, with a shout that brought his sister at a run from the house and caused the office clerks to look up from their account-books, Jacob formed a cup of his two hands and hastily drank up the dripping water.

" 'Tis fresh, sweet water!" he shouted. "Perhaps the heat drove the salt away! No!" he added, after a moment's thought. "The heat, in turning the water to steam, separated it from the salt."

Nervously, spluttering in his speech, his eyes beaming with excitement, Jacob explained to Aaron the discovery he had made. Then the two friends, forgetting for the moment their disappointment in the steamboat, hastily made a coil of copper piping. Within a few minutes clear, sweet water trickled through the funnel into a cup. The first condensing still in America had been invented!

To the gaping crowd of laborers, clerks, and servants the discovery was not of much account, but a gentleman, who had been in the office with Matthias Bush when Jacob's cry rang out came to see what had happened.

"Truly, this is a wonderful thing, for if it be so that pure water can be obtained from sea water, then never again will I have to suffer the pangs of thirst when on my voyage to Europe. Your invention will be a new flower in America's wreath," said Thomas Jefferson, Secretary of State, democratically shaking the grimy hands of the two young Jews.

Matthias Bush relieved Jacob from all other work, promising to put the distilling engine, if successful, on all his vessels. Day and night Jacob conducted his experiments with his condensation of water, rapidly improving his methods and gaining greater results thereby. He lost all track of time, and, though his sister and Aaron often spoke to him, and others came to watch, he noticed them not.

Then one day, however, as he happened to glance at the window, he saw the evil face of John Merritt peering in. His enemy entered. Looking around at the strangely rebuilt ship, the coils and kettles of the still and other appliances with which the friends had often experimented, he said mockingly: "What! Is the dreamer still inventing?"

"Get out!" demanded Jacob, striding angrily across the room.

Merritt retreated a step, saying, "Don't get excited, Jew. I have just landed from the packet, having heard that George Washington, the President, is to be in Wilmington today, and I expect an introduction to him, as I am a man of influence now. Then, as I heard you were here, I thought I would look in as I passed. What is this concoction?" he gave the still a derisive kick, "and what is in those bottles?" pointing to a row of bottles filled to the brim and sparkling in the sunlight on the window-ledge.

"Fresh, sweet water made from salt sea water from off the Delaware Capes," cried Aaron Lazarus enthusiastically.

"Ha, ha! Ho, ho! Fresh water from salt! Blood from stones! New wine from old! You Jews will set the world afire yet!" Merritt doubled up in pretended merriment. Then the door darkened as three men entered.

One glance, and all the men present bowed with eager reverence, for there stood Benjamin Franklin, the inventor-patriot, Thomas Jefferson, and the great Washington himself, whose quick ear had taken in every word.

Bowing slightly, Washington stepped toward the still. Jefferson had evidently explained its workings to him before their visit. Silently he took in all the details. He nodded pleasantly as he surveyed the bottles on the shelf.

Quickly John Merritt reached over as if to hand one of them to the President. There was an evil glint in his eyes, because he hoped the water would not prove sweet.

Washington suddenly turned to Jacob.

"Make some more, friend," he said, "I would taste it direct from your machine."

Aaron filled the iron caboose with sea water, "from three miles off the Delaware Capes, at flood-tide, sir," he explained. Then, by means of a pair of bellows, he roused the charcoal embers into a red glow, and piled on shavings. Jacob tightened down the copper cap with its straight tin tube which passed obliquely through a cask of cold water.

John Merritt began to speak disparagingly, but a stern glance from Washington silenced him, and the party waited in impressive silence. Then, drip, drip, came the water from the end of a spiral pipe into the narrow-neck bottle which Jacob's trembling fingers held under it. When filled, Jacob handed it to the President with an awkward bow.

George Washington drank to the last drop; then with Old World courtesy handed the empty bottle to Jacob, saying, "I am pleased to express myself as highly satisfied with it."

" 'Tis as pure as the best pump water in the city,"

Aaron seized Merritt by his collar.

remarked Benjamin Franklin, beaming over his huge spectacles, as he accepted the second bottle.

Thomas Jefferson smiled. "I will urge Congress to give you a sufficient award, and will request that the clearance for every vessel sailing from the ports of the United States shall be printed on a paper on the back whereof are details of this method."

"Jacob! Let's be friends," pleaded Merritt, after the President's party had left. "Let bygones be ——"

"Get out!" replied Jacob, pushing him toward the door.

"Don't be harsh, Jacob," pleaded Sarah.

"A true lady speaks—" began Merritt, bowing gracefully; but Aaron's strong hand seized him by his dandified lace collar and he almost threw the wretch out of the open door.

Crestfallen because Washington had seen his discomfiture, Merritt, cursing under his breath, brushed his clothes. "I'd like to burn this place down," he muttered to himself, "with them in it, except the girl." His face grew soft as he thought of her. Silently he stole away to plan revenge.

At last the steam-driven vessel was ready for a sea trip, for Aaron had finally produced an engine that would work. Trials up and down the river had been successful. On the morrow Aaron and Jacob planned to go out as far as the Capes.

As the dawn of a new day broke and the tide began to ebb seaward Sarah hastened to the little craft to leave a basketful of food. As she stepped down the ladder to the tiny cabin, she heard a footstep; then the gang-plank splashed into the water alongside, while the vessel, released from her moorings by some strange hand, slipped into the Delaware River. The hiss of steam and the clanking of machinery followed. Aided by the outgoing tide, the little side-paddles noisily churned the water into foam.

Puzzled and somewhat alarmed, the girl appeared on deck.

John Merritt faced her with his ever-mocking smile and cunning eyes. He had lurked in the shadows of Matthias Bush's wharves for days, gleaning knowledge of service to him in his evil plans.

Then a puff of black smoke, followed by flames, came through the window of the little shed on the boat as her brother and Aaron appeared on the wharf.

Merritt shouted in glee as he pointed to the sight. "That's how I pay my debts to the Jews! Now to the open sea with you alone!"

The girl screamed and at the sound Aaron seized a small rowboat; Jacob jumped in, and the friends began to row vigorously toward the little steam-vessel, but the success of the steam-engine was only too real, and they were left far behind.

Merritt drew an army pistol from his belt. "Go aft!" he ordered. Then as the girl found it hard to keep her feet, the rolling billows of the open sea having been reached, he tied her hand and foot to the flag-pole in spite of her struggles.

"Now, my pretty dark-eyed Jewess," he said mockingly, "a little starvation and that thirst I once encountered off these Delaware Capes will bring you to a more tractable mind. But wait! I have something that should win your favor quicker than force." Taking a packet from an inside pocket, he displayed a string of beautiful pearls. "Look how they enhance your ravishing beauty," he exclaimed as he slipped them over her head. "One little kiss and I ——"

"Look, the fire is going out," said the girl, outwardly calm.

He turned swiftly, and seeing the truth of her remark, he hastily piled on more logs, the smoke pouring densely from the little smoke-stack. Suddenly the escaping steam began to hiss shrilly from the valve.

"Curse this fool invention!" he muttered. "It makes so much noise I cannot hear the girl's sweet voice." Choosing a suitable stick from the wood-pile, he fiercely rammed it down the pipe and, by tightly wrapping a bunch of rags around the top, succeeded in stopping the noisy hiss.

Then he came toward the girl with both arms outstretched and with a leering, bantering smile that froze the blood in her veins. "Sweet one," he cried, "I want payment for my gift of pearls."

"Thief!" cried Sarah. "You stole them long ago from my father, and ——"

"True; but all the same, they are my peace-offering to the girl I ——"

His arms were around her; his hot breath made her recoil in terror. Helpless, with rescuers far away, Sarah raised her head to the brazen skies and called aloud to the God of her fathers for aid.

Then came a roar as the boiler exploded. The broken, jagged safety-valve struck Merritt in its flight, hurling him overboard; the ship twisted and broke in two as the remains of the engine disappeared. Sarah, unhurt but helplessly fastened to the flagpole, was bobbing up and down in the water, the pearls still hanging from her neck.

It seemed like hours to her when her brother's white face appeared over the top of a wave; she was quickly released from the wreckage and hauled over the side of the rescue boat.

But it was on Aaron's shoulder she nestled, while Jacob, feeling strangely weak, looked across the heaving waters with tears of happiness in his eyes and steered the boat straight for the Capes of Delaware.

"HELP! Help!!" Feebly the cry echoed through the rocky gorge.

A solitary Indian, paddling down the Charles River toward Boston settlement, one beautiful afternoon in the early springtime, heard faintly the call above the splashing of nearby falls. A few lithe movements, and the redskin, leaving his canoe, was making his way through the trackless forest toward the weak and despairing cry.

A moan reached his ears. Looking down into a defile, a strange sight met his eye. Some Indians had set a deer trap of wood-fibre rope. It was set in such a way that it would catch the foot of a passing animal and slip a noose around it. Then when the startled animal tried to free itself, the trap would spring a bent tree. A man in Puritan garb had been caught in this powerful snare.

"Heaven be praised!" he cried, as the Indian released his dislocated foot. "God has sent you. He uses even the heathen on His errands of mercy." The whining tone revealed the religious fanatic.

Pointing to the broken snare, the Puritan snarled: "That invention of Satan's, is it yours?"

The Indian bathing the swollen foot with water from a spring, glanced up at the angry eyes. "No!" he muttered sulkily. His terror-stricken face, however, seemed to denote guilt.

"You lie, you wretched savage!" Then, with a look of loathing at the kneeling figure, he muttered, "With God's help, we must root this nest of serpents out of the world."

Night was now approaching; there was no time to be lost.

"You are Squanto, the Indian?" inquired the Puritan.

"Yes," was the reply.

"Well, take me to Goodman Eliot's house. He will attend to my hurt."

Without a word the Indian paddled the canoe down the beautiful stream until the log houses of Boston came into view.

As they reached the Common a great uproar greeted them. Thousands of people surged around a row of gibbets. In the dancing torchlight the scene was weird beyond description.

The roll of the Honorable Artillery Company's

drums failed to drown the tumult; the authorities, seeking to quiet the angry populace, were almost in despair, while a Puritan minister, oblivious to the din, preached in a nasal drone to the criminals—a witch, a Quakeress, and seven pirates.

Jeremiah Parris, the Puritan, forgot his bruised foot and leaped to the bank. "What is it?" he inquired.

A surly sea-captain at the edge of the surging crowd answered, "We're tired of waiting. Seven hours has he expounded, yet the sinners show no sign of repentance. One of the pirates—he with the flower in his buttonhole—doth bow and smile to the people, and ribaldly puts fingers to nose at the reverend. 'Tis well that such should die, but the crowd liketh not that the Quaker woman should hang. The maid is sweet and gentle. If all men voted, and not you of the minority alone, she would be released after a whipping."

Parris called to the Indian in the canoe. Getting no reply, he stepped to the river's edge.

Squanto, terror-stricken, had fainted.

Surprised at the stoical Indian's strange collapse, the Puritan plunged his hand into the bosom of the Indian's deerskin jacket to feel the heart-beat, and when he withdrew his hand, there, in his palm, was a quaint gold pendant engraved with a mystic sign.

"I knew it; God be praised! 'Tis an omen!" he muttered gleefully.

The crowds were slowly dispersing and the Rev.

Mr. Mather, Bible in hand, turned from the last strangling victim of the execution with a sigh of disappointment. His preaching had been in vain.

"Satan is powerful," he remarked sadly to Parris, who had sought him out. Then, tenderly, like a mother, "Why walk you so lame?"

"Satan is indeed powerful," repeated Parris. "He lays snares for the feet of God's chosen saints. But come to the Town House, I have something of importance to reveal."

Pastor Mather—one of the nine-and-twenty Puritan ministers who bore that famous name—was the natural product of that period of intense bigotry, during which Puritanism had gone mad. The first thing this honest, but misguided shepherd of souls did on entering the spacious, oak-beamed hall of the Town House, was to grovel on the sanded floor in abject misery at his unworthiness in not being allowed to "snatch the brands from the burning" after so many hours of exhortation.

"The Prince of the Power of the Air, the Evil One, is angry tonight," remarked Parris, as a gale of wind shook the building, rattling the window casements and blowing out some of the candles.

"Yes," Mather replied. "His legions seek to overwhelm us for our presumption in punishing his witch."

"Also for my capture of a worker in black magic," announced Parris with an air of triumph.

"What!" roared Mather. "More deviltry! Who is it?"

"Squanto," replied his fellow minister. "For a long time I have been suspicious of the savage. I have imprisoned him."

"But this Indian has always been a good friend to our people," remarked Mather. "Besides, our laws govern not the savages unless they are converts, and this man is still a heathen."

"He has long been under Christian influence and is more like ourselves than any of his fellows."

"True."

"Often have I followed this savage," continued Parris, "but he doth glide where I stumble. I have seen him meet with others in bowers made of green leaves. They did feast and did blasphemously imitate the sacraments of the Church. Today, I saw him gather twelve small stones from the hillside. The Spirit told me that he was about to cast a stone at the name of each of the disciples, when I startled him. Before I could reach him, however, twelve devils clutched my foot and held me rooted to the spot; twelve more devils carried him away. I called on God for help, and He brought the Indian back who released me."

Pastor Mather leapt to his feet. His eyes blazed with the fighting aggressiveness of the intolerant Puritan. "Tomorrow is the Sabbath," he said. "We will examine this child of Satan before the congregation.

Meanwhile, we will fast and pray for the heavenly voices to guide us."

The next morning the poor Indian was awakened by the Puritans' assembling by beat of drum, each carrying his blunderbuss. A sergeant placed them three abreast. First came the Governor in a long robe, the preacher on his right hand, followed by the captain of the troops with his side-arms. Squanto and other suspects were given places, and the little column, guarded by the young men with muskets ready for instant service, moved silently to the church.

The first row of seats was allotted to those suspected of crimes and errors. During the long morning their fears and consciences were probed with tireless skill and hell was painted in colors so vivid that the weaker ones collapsed.

Then, following a short respite, the afternoon session again took up the theme. Hour after hour the spellbound congregation listened with deep satisfaction to Pastor Mather. Occasionally, a sour-faced Puritan would arise and contest the expounder's arguments, and, on every side, these strange people, note-books in hand, were putting down for future discussion the many points of the long sermon.

Suddenly, as the minister completed his description of the gallows awaiting the unrepentant sinners, even picturing with vivid eloquence the pot boiling over with tar ready to preserve their hanging bodies as a warning to others, the soldier on duty at the door was brushed aside by a man dashing in and screaming at the top of his voice, "Ye hypocrite and deceiver of God's people, come off that pulpit!"

It was another poor Quaker driven mad by the mental perversity of those days. He was finally subdued and carried away while Pastor Mather, undisturbed, continued his harangue to the desired end.

Squanto, dazed and terror-stricken, was taken back to his cell as in a dream.

He was in that condition when daylight came. John Eliot brought him fruit and tobacco, and led him before the General Court.

Pastor Mather was relating how a woman and her husband in a canoe had seen the head of a man, and, about three feet off, the tail of a cat swimming before the canoe, but no body to join them.

"Do you charge this savage with witchcraft?" inquired the aristocratic-looking Governor of Massachusetts, turning to Jeremiah Parris.

"We have a law that if any man consulteth with a familiar spirit he shall be put to death," replied the minister. "You have heard our testimony. This savage cannot deny the things we charge. His guilt is seen by the fear in his face."

Governor Winthrop arose and addressed Parris. "You have told us of your experiences and Goodman Mather has added his testimony—all of which we are in duty bound to believe. But what of the life and character of this well-known Indian?"

"We have a law," Parris sharply replied, "an old English law, by which a prisoner refusing to plead shall be pressed to death with weights. Let him, therefore, be examined for witch-spots, and if he will not plead, then let the law take its course."

"I am opposed to witchcraft punishment," said Councillor Calef boldly.

Jeremiah Parris looked at Pastor Mather significantly. This man represented the voice of the great disfranchised majority.

Addressing the Governor, Mather said, "This new world was the undisturbed realm of Satan until our settlements were made. It is but natural, therefore, that the Devil should make a peculiar effort to bring moral destruction on us, the godly invaders."

"The logic would be conclusive," remarked John Eliot, "if we knew the ancestry of the Indians."

The kindly disposed members were overruled, however. Squanto was seized, and although needles failed to discover witch-marks—spots insensible to pain—great rocks were piled on his stomach. His agony was terrible; the heavy weights forced his tongue from his mouth. Pastor Mather pushed it back with his cane. The Indian's appealing eyes moved the heart of the Governor, who, by a wave of his hand, and in spite of the mutterings of the fanatics, stopped the torture.

John Eliot raised the poor bruised body. Eloquent eyes thanked him.

"These savages should be wiped out of this land," snarled the disappointed Mather. "Even as God led the Children of Israel out of bondage into Canaan, so has He freed us from Pharaoh's grip and led us across the Red Sea to this new land. He has given us ——"

"Wait!" interrupted John Eliot. "God sent these Indians here before we came. What if they are His chosen people?"

"You refer to the lost ten tribes of Israel?" Mather asked, his eyes sparkling with interest.

"I do," replied John Eliot.

"I agree with him," Judge Sewall vigorously announced. "I have long believed it."

"Truly, my studies lead to that conclusion, also," admitted Pastor Mather thoughtfully, while the Governor nodded assent.

"Yes, yes! That's the truth!" suddenly exclaimed the Indian, the light of hope shining in his eyes. "I am not an Indian; I am a Jew!"

Several jumped to their feet in astonishment and alarm, while Governor Winthrop said sternly: "What do you mean? If you are a Jew, how came you here before us?"

"Listen to my story, O Single Tongue," said the Indian, stretching out his arms appealingly toward the Governor. "My name is Solomon Franco. I was born in Frankfort, Germany, on the River Main. In the anti-Jewish riots there, Rabbi Jesaja Hurwitz

28

fled with me, his little pupil, down the river. Oh, those horrible, fearful days!" Overcome by his memories, he would have fallen, if Eliot had not caught him. Quickly recovering, he continued: "We fell into the hands of Rhine robber-barons; then a troop of Spanish cavalry from Holland destroyed their castle, and I was carried away as a slave by one of the officers. Next I became powder-boy, first on the *Santa Maria* galleon, then on the English ship of Captain John Smith when he destroyed the Spaniard on one of his voyages to New England. The broken water barrel that I slept in was cast overboard one winter's night in this bay when Captain Smith charted this coast, and I was saved by Samoset, the Indian. His tribe adopted me, pronouncing my name Squanto. So kind were they, and so full of horror were my earliest recollections, that I have lived in terror of falling into the hands of white men again.

"The Indians in many ways follow the teachings of my fathers. Goodman Parris speaks of our bowers of green. 'Tis the Feast of Tabernacles; the twelve stones he saw me gather were for an altar, and ——"

"Thou hast a lying tongue," interrupted Parris. "Satan is crafty, and ever seeks to deceive the godly. Here is a witch-token. I found it in his bosom." He displayed the gold trinket.

Governor Winthrop looked at it. " 'Tis a Masonic emblem," he said. "It bears a mystic word of the great Solomon. Where did you get this, Squanto?"

"Rabbi Hurwitz gave it to me as I was torn from his grasp by Spanish soldiers. 'Tis my only connection with the past."

"I met Rabbi Hurwitz in Turkey," remarked Captain Miles Standish, who was on a visit from the Plymouth colony. "He related his experiences to me; they coincide with Squanto's."

"God be praised that Rabbi Hurwitz escaped!" exclaimed Franco, the Jew.

"Amen!" devoutly murmured Winthrop and Eliot in unison.

The Puritan divines were nonplussed. The charge of witchcraft would have to be dropped. Judge Sewall came to the rescue.

"The Jew hath deceived the colony; for his duplicity he deserves death. As an unbeliever he can no longer remain here lest he bring the judgment of God upon us."

"Death to the Jew!" cried the Puritan ministers.

"Wait!" The valiant Calef sprang to his feet. "Who drove this Jew into exile?" he demanded, banging the table with his fist. "We, the followers of the Jew! Who welcomed our Pilgrim Fathers that winter's day with a word of greeting in their own tongue? Squanto, the Indian—Franco, the Jew!

"Who taught us, fed us, saved us and sat with us at our first Thanksgiving feast? This exiled, unwanted Jew!

"Who warned us of Indian treachery and made a

peace-pact with his tribe on our behalf because he thought we loved his Israel of the past? This Squanto! This unthanked Jew!

"He came to us to learn our tongue more fully and our Israelitish manners because our Sabbath was his Sabbath, too.

"Shame on you! The narrowness of your minds doth close your hearts, and ——"

"Stop!" Governor Winthrop ordered. "What you have said is true and is sufficient. What are we to do with this man, Franco?"

John Eliot arose; speaking slowly, his gentle face aflame with missionary enthusiasm, he said: "Henceforth, I will be an 'apostle' to the Indians. I will go out and gather them in—these remnants of Israel. They shall choose able men among themselves, appointing heads over their people, rulers of hundreds, of fifties, and of tens."

"You shall have Walnut Hill plantation," said the Governor, strangely moved.

"And money without stint!" a wealthy shipmaster exclaimed.

"And our prayers," added Judge Sewall, after a moment's thought.

"God moves in a mysterious way His wonders to perform," said Mather slowly. "We have been hasty; our zeal hath led us astray, I fear. May God forgive us!"

"Amen!" said Parris with unusual emphasis.

Therefore, the books of the General Court record, in quaint old English, the following:

"This court allows Solomon Franco, the Jew, six shillings per week out of the treasury for ten weeks for subsistence till he can get his passage into Holland."

On the same page appears another entry:

"This court grants John Eliot twelve square miles for an Indian plantation and the sum of £10 to prosecute the work of organizing the ideal government of the ancient Jewish state among the Indians thereon. Squanto, the Indian, shall there assist John Eliot in translating the Holy Bible into the Indian dialect."

At the close of a summer's day, two men, resting in the shade of a giant oak, contemplated busy Natick, the first of the "praying Indian" villages to arise on Israel's foundations.

"God has been good to us, Squanto!" remarked John Eliot, apostle to the Indians.

"Praised be His Holy Name," replied Franco, the Jew.

"AND your sister is grievously sick." Jacob Lumbrozo, physician, planter, and trader, folded the letter with a sigh. From the balcony of his magnificent home he glanced over the golden panorama of that autumn day in 1658. There were great manor-houses set in fields of ripening tobacco, amid gardens of fruit and flowers, bounded by forests whose distant purpled treetops met the sky—a land of comfort, where no pale ghost of starving want ever stalked, a land of Catholic government, but where sweet tolerance ruled, for even he, oft called "Ye Jew Doctor," lived happily and undisturbed.

As the merry sounds of his young wife's ball, the music of harpsichord, violins, and dancing feet, floated out on the fragrant air, his thoughts went back to days of terror in the capital city of Portugal. "Maryland, my Maryland," he lovingly murmured.

A quiet step and the strong arm of John Washington, his Virginia friend, who had been a fellow immigrant two years before, passed around his shoulder. "Yes, friend Jacob," he said, " 'tis indeed beauteous; one could die fighting for its safety, if need be. But why are you sad?"

" 'Tis this letter from Holland. Our great rabbi, Manasseh ben Israel, has just died, and the beloved sister I left in his care lies sick ——"

"I thought, perhaps, you were overmuch worried by the threats of that fierce Jesuit whose arguments you did so strongly withstand."

"I was foolish to debate with him, for he has sought to entrap me since I witnessed against him in the courts last year. But here comes the Deputy-Governor's coach."

The carriage stopped at the broad marble steps; an obsequious negro opened the door and Thomas Greene, the Governor's Deputy, stepped out, followed by one whose fierce eyes and extraordinarily high cheek-bones covered with parchment-like skin denoted the religious fanatic.

"Jacob Lumbrozo, Jewish heretic," he snapped, through lips as thin as a rat-trap. "I denounce you as a blasphemer!"

Thomas Greene had a crafty eye and a selfish look in his weak face. He desired to please the powerful Jesuit, of whom even the Catholics lived in awe. This Jesuit had appeared that morning before the Deputy-Governor with charges against the Jew.

"Yes, indeed, Lumbrozo, thou shalt be made to answer this awful charge," said Greene.

"I am willing," quietly replied the Jew.

"But this is absurd!" cried John Washington, Jacob Lumbrozo's friend, lithely springing down the steps in one bound.

The Governor retreated to his carriage; but the Jesuit faced John Washington contemptuously, and said, "Men like you never count for much; it is we who plan and toil while you eat and drink, dance and sleep ——"

"Patience, John," pleaded Lumbrozo. "For two years we have lived here; all men know us; unjust accusations will fall of their own weight. Let Father Time clear this matter," he concluded, as with a calm smile he placed his hand on a honeysuckle-covered sun-dial.

"At the State House, then, tomorrow morning," Thomas Greene called from the window of the coach as it drove away.

John Washington turned to his friend. "There lies Virginia and my home," he pointed across the Poto-mac. It was a suggestion to flee from Maryland.

"My honor will not permit," was the quiet reply. "Sooner or later the testing time comes for every standard-bearer of our race in these new settlements. I will not fail in Maryland, though ruin and death itself await me."

"As you will, but fear not; the Catholics are tolerant and kind, and Lord Baltimore ———"

"Truly, the Catholics of Maryland are, indeed, Christians," the Jew remarked whimsically; "but Father Matthews and I are men of Lisbon, and you know not what that means. Their scheming ———"

"We, too, can counter-scheme, as you shall see," whispered his friend as he departed. "Fear not!"

Jacob Lumbrozo, greatly depressed and realizing the unrelenting hate of his powerful foes, spent the night in preparing for the worst. Morning broke over scenes of indescribable beauty, but the necessity of giving final instructions to his many tenants, laborers, and servants took up so much time that the sun was high in the heaven as he galloped down sleepy Middle Street of the plantations' little village—the county seat of St. Mary's. The only sound heard was that of his horse's hoofs on the cobblestones.

Fastening his steed to one of the many shady chestnut trees, he entered the massive State House. A few minutes later the "thirty choice musketeers of St. Mary's" assembled at the roll of the drum, and the charge of blasphemy, the worst of all charges in those days, was hurled at Jacob Lumbrozo by his enemies.

The accused man glanced over the crowded court. Many friends were absent, he noticed; but, on every hand, smiling nods came from many a Catholic as well as from Protestants. But the zealous missionaries of the Church ruled with a heavy hand. Andrew White, the aged Father Superior, was speaking:

"On St. Andrew's Day all the sprites and witches of this land were set against us in battle array in the clouds; a fearful wind so quickly ripped the sails of our ships—the *Ark* and the *Dove*—that even the stout hearts of the sailors quailed. Being helpless, we fell to prayer, confessions and vows.

"All night Heaven and Hell fought over us, till at length Father Fitzherbert, discovering the wicked spirit hiding among us under the guise of an old woman, we hanged her and it pleased God to send some ease. With the rising of the sun over the heaving waters, God, in His goodness, delivered our Mary Land to His Holy Church, after seven weeks on the seas.

"On Our Blessed Lady's Day we first offered the Holy Sacrifice, erected a cross, and with devotions took possession for God and His Church. Then did the heretics and blasphemers come—" The trembling priest sat down, overcome by his emotions. Honest, zealous, the dangers to his beloved faith were very real.

The falling standard was seized by Father Matthews, "And shall we hand the heritage given to us by God to schismatic heretics and blasphemous Jews?" His voice, cold and hard as steel, rang out a challenge to his people.

"But the evidence?" timidly ventured the judge.

"We will come to that," said the priest, turning a scowling face to the questioner, who meekly bowed his acquiescence.

"We have a law," continued the Jesuit, "that whosoever shall deny our Savior to be the Son of God shall be punished with death, and the heretic's lands and goods be confiscated. I will present the evidence of this Jew's guilt, demand his death, and claim for the Church his wealth."

"I have no wealth," remarked Lumbrozo quietly.

"Thy manor lands?" inquired the inquisitor.

"They are not mine. All land in Maryland is the property of the proprietor, Lord Baltimore, now in England. The Indians, knowing little of white men's ways, in their gratitude gave me land, which I innocently took. The Governor, even now, is considering the matter."

"Then our lands, given to us by Indian grants ——"

"Are illegally held," Lumbrozo bluntly concluded, and the audience gave vent to amused titters.

"Lord Baltimore is a true son of the Church," said a priest sharply, "he will submit to our decisions in the matter."

"And thy goods, Lumbrozo?" inquired the judge sarcastically.

"I have no goods. All I have belongs to my sister in Holland, save that which is my wife's, and she is not a Jewess."

"How came you here?"

"I was a Portuguese court physician until your people ruled that it were better for the king to die than be cured by a Jew. But because I did leave instructions for healing potions before I was exiled and refused payment in return, the king did give my sister a necklace of rare beauty. This she pawned with my people to establish a home in this sunny southland of America."

"A pretty story," sneered the baffled priest, "and who can verify it?"

"I can!" a voice came from the window, as a man leaned over the sill. "I, Captain James Neale, of Wolleston Manor, after fourteen years in Lisbon as the agent of King Charles, have returned and can vouch for the words of the Jew!"

The Jesuits were disturbed and angry. Their supremacy was endangered.

Father Matthews arose. "The Church is menaced!" he cried. "An example must be made of the Jew, for he is the most prominent of his people. We know Jacob Leah, David Fereira, Mathias de Sousa, Mathias de Costa, Isaac de Barrette, and that dark-eyed Jewess—Hester Cordea, the most stubborn of them all."

Then he, at great length, related the conversation upon which the trial for blasphemy was being held.

"The Jew is guilty," announced the judge. "His property shall be given to the Church, and his life shall pay forfeit on the gallows after ten days' grace."

"Amen!" chanted Father Matthews.

As the hard, cruel voice re-echoed from the bare walls, brave faces paled and tears came to the eyes of women. Maryland was grieved!

But hark! From the nearby fort the cannon's voice roared, and at that moment into the tense courtroom staggered the dusty figure of Nicholas Causine, a soldier, bleeding from mortal wounds.

"Arm! Arm! The Protestants are rebelling! The Virginians are coming! 'Hey for St. Mary's!'" The war-cry of Maryland ended in a death sob.

But scores took up the cry and rushed out behind their musketeers.

Dr. Lumbrozo, hustled into the adjacent prison, saw through the barred window and across the gallows' green a small party of Virginians, led by John Washington, storm the fort. "In the name of God, fall on!" they cried. Maryland Protestants from their settlement at nearby Providence were putting torch to the Governor's residence, the beautiful palace of St. John's.

"Down with the Jesuits!" shrieked a man, brandishing his sword and leading a party of sailors toward the State House. Thirty muskets replied from the smashed windows of the building. Checked by this unexpected reply, the sailors fled to shelter, leaving William Clayborne, a Protestant fanatic and the evil genius of the colony, writhing in agony among the fallen leaves.

With the fort captured and the palace in flames, the entire body of rebels surrounded the State House, where the Jesuits, recognizing their helplessness, surrendered.

"All hail the Republic of Maryland!" cried Josiah Fendall, leader of all the Protestants.

"But Charles, the King—" began Thomas Greene, the Governor's Deputy, protestingly.

"Was executed!" Fendall finished the sentence. "The monarchy has fallen! Long live Oliver Cromwell, the Protector! There is a Commonwealth in England; we want one here."

"Long live the Republic!" The cry re-echoed through the mulberry groves, and Dr. Lumbrozo in his prison, hearing the sound, wondered how it would affect his fate.

He was not long in doubt. Through the barred window he saw the black-robed Jesuits expelled from Maryland forever. Bound with chains, but with the noble air of martyrs, they were led down to the water's edge, where a boat carried them midstream to a waiting ship.

Again brought before the court, Lumbrozo found his position unchanged, for Josiah Fendall, taking the place vacated by the terrified Deputy-Governor Thomas Greene, was under the influence of the intolerant Protestant element whose fierce fanaticism had caused them to be exiled from the settlements in Virginia. Welcomed by the kindly people of Maryland, the intriguers, by taking advantage of the Protestant uprising, had seized the reins of authority, and now, in their hour of victory, were merciless toward all their opponents.

"Friend Fendall," cried Wilkinson, the Quaker, "the Spirit calls upon us to purge this hotbed of Popery of all unrighteousness, and this Jew hath denied that our Lord hath come in Jesus; he hath indeed broken the law of Maryland."

Fendall nodded in approval. "I will administer the laws as I find them until new ones are made," he announced a moment later. "Let the Jew's sentence stand!"

A sudden commotion at the door, and there appeared a gentleman of culture and breeding. "Lord Baltimore! The Governor!" a dozen voices cried in astonishment.

"I have a message from the Lord High Chancellor of England, signed by His Holiness, the Pope. Usurper, read it!" Half-humorously he pushed the document signed with the Great Seal of England and the Papal arms into the hands of the unwilling judge, who glanced with almost comic horror at the two great seals attached to the one document.

It was the ruling of England, acknowledged by the *Congregatio de Propaganda Fide*, the superiors of the Jesuit order in Rome, establishing Lord Baltimore as sole owner of all the lands of Maryland, with the right of disposal of the same.

"Where are my recently-arrived tenants, the Jesuits?" he asked.

"Expelled!" snapped Fendall.

"And what is the charge against my friend Lumbrozo?"

"He has ignored and violated the Toleration Act in denying Jesus is the true Messiah. The penalty is death. Do you favor clemency?" Fendall's sneer conveyed a threat.

Lord Baltimore gaily took a pinch from his golden snuff-box with a flourish. His mind was working rapidly. In triumphant eyes he saw angry seas of hatred threatening his beloved colony. The zealots of his own dear faith were expelled, leaving the people as sheep without shepherds. His beautiful home was in ruins; himself virtually a prisoner, while his life might pay forfeit for one false step, even as that of Charles, his King, had done.

Bending to the storm, he would trust the God of his fathers who had given him the colony to restore and increase, in His own good time, the prosperity of the settlement. He considered it unwise, therefore, to antagonize the evil men now in the saddle.

"Let the sentence stand, if you wish!" the Governor replied quietly.

A wave of dismay swept over the room among both Protestant and Catholic commoners who felt friendly toward the hounded Jew. Fendall was disappointed and angry, for he had hoped to place the odium of

Lumbrozo's death upon Lord Baltimore. "Away with the prisoner!" he shouted.

"I thought it wise to keep my coming secret," remarked the well-beloved Governor to his people. "There is much I could tell you—but let events shape themselves; I await God's own good pleasure!"

Day followed day and the time grew short. The prisoner was allowed only two visitors, John Washington and Lord Baltimore, who both sought to divert his thoughts. Across the green, however, he saw his people, his loved friends of every creed, and the loyal workers of his plantations. His prostrated wife was too ill to visit him.

The Virginians had returned to their side of the Potomac. John Washington alone remained, faithful to the end.

When the day of fate dawned, a clear, crisp morning, Lumbrozo was awakened by the men on the green making final preparations. Again the "thirty choice musketeers" were on guard duty. Many morbid-minded fanatics arrived early, Quakers, Catholics, Puritans, and others who ever enjoyed scenes of religious intolerance. The fresh breeze from the open Chesapeake had brought a white-sailed ship from overseas. He idly wondered who was on it. Then the sun rose above the hills and flooded the scene with golden beauty. A tramp of armed men; a bugle rang out. "The hour has come," he murmured.

To the gathering crowds, however, a herald's voice

44

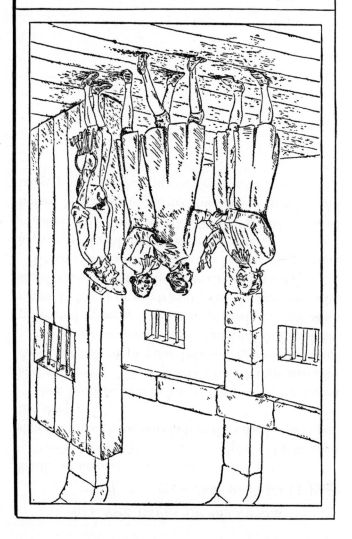

They were your father's boys.

cried out: "Long live Cromwell, Protector of England! Let amnesty be granted all prisoners!"

"You're free! You're free!" John Washington shouted through the bars before the guard could open the door.

Then Lord Baltimore kissed the Jew on the cheek and whispered, "Thou shouldst be a happy man, indeed, for this morn your babe—a boy—was born."

For a few moments Jacob Lumbrozo's happiness prevented speech. Then, "John shall be my son's name, in honor of my friend John Washington, who stood by me so faithfully in the day of trouble."

Up the narrow path from the landing stage came a woman—Lumbrozo's own dear sister.

Amid the cheers of friends, the fastest team of horses in Maryland carried him home to wife and babe, prosperity, happiness, peace, and love.

VIRGINIA was the mother of the English colonies, and the City of London the mother of Virginia. London was the heart, and old Father Thames the great artery of England. Along the northern side of that river, threading its way among vast and gloomy warehouses stored with the wealth of nations and ending abruptly at the moat of London's ancient castle, ran the Tower street.

A weird, aromatic, elusive perfume of spices, drugs, hides, rare woods and a multitude of other things pervaded murky portals and hovered as if in silent protest about an obnoxious new sign, "Ye Tobacco Rolle," the sign which bore witness that the nation was fast falling at the shrine of that strange new goddess, Our Lady Nicotine.

Here lived in silent, solemn state the King's collector of customs, one whose name was not given to the world, his race being proscribed, but who was known to his many visitors as "Mr. Jacobs of Virginia."

If one had kept watch, he would have been surprised at the name and quality of his many visitors. Here came many of the personal agents of James, the King; Sir Walter Raleigh, fallen into disgrace and pitiful need; Admiral Hawkins, bringing the necklace Queen Bess had given when fortune smiled; and John Rolfe, with the first Virginian tobacco. Many a privateer-captain brought his lists of captured treasures. Here came bluff and honest John Smith, soldier of fortune, making light of his Turkish captivity and boasting of his combats with man and nature. From here he went to aid the struggling colony of Virginia and to find a new England.

But the visitors were not all of high renown. Sometimes, from a weather-beaten ship, haggard refugees, evading the river guards and the city's night watch, would find a welcome at this silent, gloomy house. By ones and twos the members of persecuted races and hunted sects, grasping tattered scraps of parchment on which the Custom House address was scribbled, the magnet of many a longing heart in the lands of darkest tyranny. The refugees would reach the haven, starved, wounded and lame, prematurely aged and mentally well-nigh wrecked, but happy in the safety of their children, whom they hugged with piteous passion.

From behind the golden sign, invisible influences reached out through Holland, Spain and Turkey to the Far East and to the Western World, as map-makers, merchants, diplomats, explorers, financiers, churchmen, sea-captains and soldiers of fortune came and went.

A broad-shouldered little man, his dark hair tipped with silver, sat in the tiny living-room office behind the resplendent sign. He conferred often with others of his race, his face aglow as he carried on the war against tyranny. He juggled with the jealousies, fears and ambitions of Czar, Sultan, Pope and rulers. He lost, but played again, with Time and Humanity ever on his side.

Once upon a time his motive had been revenge. Some years before, on a certain day in January, an *auto da fé* had been held at Lisbon, Portugal, in which one hundred and fifty Jews and Jewesses literally walked in the shadow of death, and were set free from that fearful procession only at the last moment on payment of an enormous fine.

Standing on the cobblestoned plaza, with his delicate, pale-faced little wife by his side, surrounded by sorrowful groups of his own people, raging anger had surged in his soul as they awaited the awful ordeal.

The ransom money paid, however, all these poor victims of the Inquisition hastened to leave the land which bigotry had made intolerable for them. Broken in health and ruined in fortune, they made for the friendly shores of Holland.

Unfavorable winds, followed by a great storm in the English Channel, scattered the vessels carrying the refugees; the husband was separated from his wife—who was traveling on a larger and more comfortable ship—and he found himself in a small seaport on the southern coast of England.

Though separated from his fellow Israelites, he had one good friend who stood by him in the day of trouble, Edward Nicholas, a well-disposed young gentile, an assistant warden of the Cinque Ports, through whom his travel arrangements had been made.

The equinoctial storms continued, however, and all sea travel ceased for the time being. When the weather did abate, definite word came from Amsterdam that the ship on which his wife had traveled had sunk with all on board. Letters from friends, eyewitnesses of the dismasted vessel wallowing in the trough of the great seas, gave him no hope.

His kindly friend Nicholas sought to console the Jew as best he could. Edward Nicholas was a man of much youthful enthusiasm and energy and greatly interested in trade, shipping, and commerce. To turn the poor man's distraught mind from the sorrows that had come upon him, he attempted to arouse his friend's interest in these fields of activity and service and pointed to the undoubted fact that intolerance toward the Jew in England, after long centuries of ostracism, was fading, that a door was slowly opening for Israel in the budding Empire that was to replace that of Spain.

The shrewd dark eyes of the Jew, however, saw more hope in the New World and though, thanks to the influence of his powerful friend, he stayed in England more or less secretly, the American colonies became the center of his interest.

As he sat in his upholstered chair, many whispered hearsays and bruited rumors brought him strange and wonderful news, and the Old World gave way more and more in his mind to the beckoning new one. America became the center of all his plans, "the hope of Israel," as he told the rabbis of the Continent, and Virginia was to be the mother of all the struggling English colonies in the New World. Thus he became known as "Mr. Jacobs of Virginia."

Several of King James' courtiers had sought to revive the waning hatred toward his race by telling their ruler of the Jews' growing strength in England's trade and commerce. Mr. Jacobs smiled at the thought. If they only knew the fullness of that truth!

Some of these same courtiers had even gone to Virginia, captained by the brave pioneer John Smith. They expected to find gold and jewels as plentiful as dirt, and to build themselves palaces in the virgin woods. They took footmen and lackeys, with silks and satins, rich wines, and dainty laces.

A few of these adventurous Englishmen struggled into real manhood there, but most of them had collapsed under the strain of pioneer life. Some returned to London with Captain John Smith to seek further financial aid for the Virginian plantations.

But here, this morning, while thick yellow fog, like an evil genie, rose from filthy mud-flats, and the clammy chill of November penetrated even the rich, heavy tapestries of his cozy office-home, the spirit of "Mr. Jacobs of Virginia" drooped. He watched the logs burn low, as his thoughts wandered, recalling many a somber scene.

The fire died out; thin wisps of fog found their way through cracks in the window casements; their ghostly fingers clutching his throat, aroused him. He threw straw into the grate and emptied the scuttle of sea-coal. Its cheerful blaze aroused in him the fighting spirit of his people; his dark eyes sparkled.

"Wherefore are we sad?" he inquired of his ever-faithful companion, a great dog, a gift from the kindly monks of St. Bernard, in the frozen Alps, whose stock of rare cordials he had once replenished. "The God of Israel liveth," he cried, "and hath given us a golden gate of opportunity. It must be kept open!" He opened the door. "Joseph!" he called.

Joseph Moise, a young French refugee of his own race, bounded up the stairs.

"I would have you leave for Virginia," said his master quietly.

"I go willingly." The soft answer denoted an adoring faith in the man whose outstretched hand had saved not only him and many others of his own race, but many of the persecuted Huguenots as well.

"You may go to certain death or imprisonment. The Indians have swept the settlements, massacring the sick, discouraged, and starving settlers by hundreds. You will escape the Indian peril, however; the Government will exterminate them. The laws of Moses will protect you against the plague; but Governor Argall is a Puritan bigot, and death awaits all who deny the Trinity. The time has come for one of our race to take his stand for the God of Israel."

"When do I leave, Seignior?" The voice sought to be courageous, but the elder's sharp eye pierced the boy's brave front; arms flew open, and with the cry as of a wounded animal, the youth was smothered in the flowing dressing-gown of his benefactor. They kissed like sire and son, while the lad sobbed, "Must I leave you; must I go?"

The strong man turned abruptly away. Then, after a moment's silence, he curtly commanded, "Inform the King I have news from Madrid; Captain Smith has just returned from America—send him to me; ask the officers of the Virginia Company to see me. Their colony will not last the year out if ——"

The St. Bernard slunk out of the room. It was no time to linger when his master was thus aroused.

✿　✿　✿

The officers of the Virginia Company met with blanched faces. "Our money," they moaned; "we have spent a fortune, gaining nothing in return—no gold, no near route to India and China, and this tobacco—a rank poisonous weed which, for the moment, hath become the national whim—angers both King and Church. This awful massacre, too! Who will emigrate now? It were better to withdraw from this venture and finance expeditions to capture galleons on the Spanish Main ——"

"The days of Spanish treasure are over," the Jew's voice was sharp and decisive.

"What shall we do?" whined a stout, comfortable-looking alderman, perspiration breaking out on his forehead.

"A better day dawns for Virginia, gentlemen," the voice was soothing and encouraging. "Seek not the pot of gold at the rainbow's end, but give heed to the natural wealth of the plantation. The danger from the savages is over, for John Rolfe is to marry the daughter of their king, and ——"

"God forbid!" ejaculated a long-faced divine, amid the general surprise at this astounding news. "Such a union would be a crime against Christianity and nature itself."

Ignoring the interruption, the speaker continued, "Virginia needs housewives and homes; send one hundred worthy girls. The colony needs young men and maidens; gather the vagrant, homeless youth

54

that idle and beg in our streets; send them to the new land of golden opportunity. In tens, fifties, and hundreds, give them land at the end of their service-time. 'Twill profit you."

And it came to pass as he had said. Ships left England soon after, carrying the future wives of Virginia's pioneers and many companies of children. Joseph Moise, with one hundred boys, sailed on the *Diana*. Something of the executive ability of his beloved benefactor had been absorbed into the nature of the young Frenchman as he attended the wants of his young charges. The weather was bad, but the winds favorable. Early in April, a gentle breeze wafted them up a river. The forts, churches, and cabins of palisaded King James' Town came into view.

Fearful of Indian treachery, the *Diana* anchored in midstream, near a coasting vessel from Brazil.

While Joseph was idly watching the ever-changing scene, another young man, evidently of gentle birth, being clad in fine lace and ruffles, waved a friendly greeting from the other ship.

"I am Elias Legardo," he cried, "brother of Jacob Legardo, the Jewish author of Brazil. I was sent here to welcome Joseph Moise. Are you ——?"

"Yes! Yes!" The newcomer leapt with joy at the knowledge that he was not to face Puritan bigotry alone. Instinctively he recognized the influence of his dear Seignior, now so far away.

"Then I'm coming aboard," Legardo again called.

He ran back a few yards on the high Spanish poop, leapt through the air and landed lightly in the rigging of the little English ship. Shrill shouts of applause came from the boy passengers, while hordes of swooping sea-gulls took to the skies.

Elias, with one hand over his heart, swept his plumed hat off in a graceful bow. "Legardo, the lizard, for such is my name in Spanish, is honored, gentlemen!"

In a few minutes he was the center of a clustering, chattering group of boys who, from that moment, adored him.

"I was always in trouble down in the South," he admitted to Joseph that evening as they sat in the log cabin of their employer, John Rolfe, the young tobacco planter. A simple-minded old crone named Rebecca, muttering harmlessly, busied herself with the needs of her greatly increased family. From a nearby cabin came that noisy chatter that ever betokens a colony of young people, the first hundred who would labor in the manifold departments of Rolfe's activity.

Elias was burnishing a breastplate of steel, for though armor, with the introduction of gunpowder, was out of date in England, it was welcomed in Virginia. The volatile young man was preparing for service against the savages.

"Yes," he continued, "they said I disturbed my bookworm brother, and so the Seignior Jacobs of Virginia, as he is often called, advised them to send me here to labor in the service of Master Rolfe; but—" he breathed lovingly on the shining steel, and his eyes flashed in sympathy as candlelight struck the metal.

"'Twas good of the Seignior to think of me—" began Joseph, but he got no further. A little Indian maid, accompanied by a silent sagamore, stood at the door. Elias dropped the armor and stared amazedly at the girl. Then, recovering, he made his most graceful bow.

The happy smile of Matoaka, daughter of the Indian King Powhatan—and known to the white men as "the little Tomboy," or in the Indian language, "Pocahontas"—was most fascinating.

"The most beautiful maid I ever saw," Elias said later to his friend. He kicked the armor contemptuously. "I don't think I'll need that." Then, shyly, "My brother says, Joseph, that the Indians came to this land long ago and are the remnants of our Lost Ten Tribes. I wonder if ——"

But his companion's snores disturbed him, so he spent most of the night looking at the moon, his head filled with strange, new ideas.

John Rolfe, a kind and considerate master, allowed the newcomers to sleep off their weariness and smilingly ignored their apologies.

"I am happy," he said at breakfast, "for today Pocahontas becomes my bride."

Elias suddenly choked, and again sought comfort in the steel cuirass.

Joseph asked about Rebecca, who was busy among the boys.

"She was one of the prisoners surrendered by the Indians after a peace treaty had been made with them," replied Rolfe. "From what little we could learn, Rebecca had been brought up from the Southland colonies of the Spaniards by a wandering or fleeing tribe of Indians from there. Methinks she is of your race—an exile from Spain or Brazil perhaps."

An Indian call came soft and low. John Rolfe almost fell over the armor as he hastened to the door.

Pocahontas' shy smile rewarded him; she nodded coyly to Joseph, laughed at Elias, and threw her arms around Rebecca. "My dearest foster-mother," she cried.

"My sweet namesake," sobbed the old lady.

When the embrace ended, Pocahontas was wearing a necklace of silver beads that Rebecca had deftly slipped over her head. " 'Tis all I have, dear one," she whispered. "But, remember, you receive my name in Christian baptism upon your marriage to John Rolfe."

But time was passing. The marriage was to take place that morning, and the vessel, returning, would take Rolfe and the Princess Rebecca to England.

❊   ❊   ❊

Mr. Jacobs of Virginia was in his office-home a few weeks later, sipping his morning coffee and glancing over *Ye Weekly Newes*, England's first newspaper, when he saw the announcement of the arrival of the Indian Princess—now Mistress Rebecca Rolfe—and her stalwart husband.

" 'Tis of little importance," he muttered. "Shall I visit the ship or not?" he asked the dog, who, in reply, wagged his tail and pawed at the door.

"That settles it," he said good-humoredly, "maybe you need a run in the good spring air."

Wending his way through the tobacco, timber, and other cargo, being unloaded, the Jew was met by the smiling John Rolfe, who introduced his shy and retiring bride.

Mr. Jacobs' piercing glance passed swiftly over the form of the demure Indian maiden, and came to rest on the silver beads around her neck. He caught his breath in amazement; he stepped forward and his trembling fingers touched the beads caressingly.

"Where did you get that?" he gasped.

"My Rebecca gave it to me," wonderingly replied the Indian girl.

The Jew said nothing.

He made a few inquiries as to the state of affairs in Virginia. Then after welcoming words of greeting, he crossed the river. Soon a swift carrier-pigeon, flying direct to Plymouth, halted his vessel, the *Jacob*, which was on its way to Virginia.

The swiftest horses of the kingdom took him by the great south highway. From the cliffs he saw his ship approaching and went out to meet it in a waterman's boat.

* * *

Joseph Moise, idly listening to Elias' Brazilian adventures, was in a reverie, when the door opened, and in stepped the man of his thoughts!

The newcomer glanced quickly around. "Rebecca!" he called. "Rebecca! 'Tis I, your husband, Moses Nehemiah!"

The little old lady suddenly appeared, shook her head as though to cast off restraining bands, and with a cry that touched the hearts of even the little lads who came crowding into the room, she was folded in her husband's embrace.

"I have been feigning madness so long since we were so cruelly separated," she whimpered, "that I forgot I was merely playing a part."

"But your ship—it did not sink, Rebecca mine?"

"No, dear one, it did not. Though it became a dismasted, leaking wreck, it outlived the storm. After many days we drifted on to Emden beach, at the mouth of a German river, and we knew we were safe. But we had no news of you, and when they told me that your little ship must have gone down in that awful tempest, my mind became a blank, for I felt that even our God had forsaken us."

"That He has never done—thanks be His holy name!" cried her husband, clasping the little silver-haired lady to his bosom. "But how come you here, my Rebecca?"

"When we finally arrived at Amsterdam and one told me that she had seen your vessel sink and that there was no hope, a party of our people who were setting out immediately for the new Arapok colony in Brazil—it was to be known as the New Amsterdam—invited me to go with them. Passively and hopelessly, I accepted their kind offer. But Lawrence Keymis' little expedition met disaster; then came storms, Spanish pirates, and Indian warfare in the Florida plantations, all of which is but a continuous horrid nightmare, but through it all the God of Israel ——"

"Brought us together," concluded her husband. For a long time, overcome by emotion, both husband and wife remained silent, then:

"We will stay in King James' Town, my dear," said he, "and nevermore will disaster or catastrophe by land or sea disturb our happy lives."

"But the Governor's laws?" inquired Joseph Moise, who had been standing by, suddenly recalling an ever-threatening peril and thinking only of his benefactor's safety.

"A new governor has been appointed; Argall will be recalled in a few days for bribery and corruption."

ON THE 9th day of November of the year 1653, the good ship, *Pear Tree*, entered Coenties' Slip, New Amsterdam, and we, Jacob Aboab and Jacob Barsimson (the writer of this account), the first two sons of Israel to enter this new gateway to a New World, did humbly pray that the God of Abraham, Isaac, and Jacob guide and protect us as we faced our unknown future.

How earnestly did Manasseh ben Israel beseech us, when he bade us godspeed in Holland, so to conduct ourselves that our good report should open a welcome door for the oppressed people of our race!

Much could be written of these stirring times—of Van Tromp leading our convoy, his mainmast-head carrying a broom to announce the sweeping of the English from the seas; of the terrible sea-fight and his death; of our long voyage; of scurvy, mutiny, storms, and many other things. But this is a simple account of how two young men of a persecuted people fared in a new land—how we found the savages and pioneers of the New World far kinder than the princes and powers of the Old.

Jacob Aboab was by my side, his thin, weak hand trembled on my arm. From the ship's deck we viewed the little city, with the windmill on the knoll, the Battery Fort, its drill-ground so smooth and green after raging seas, the great Stuyvesant farm with spired church and schoolhouse, the Bouwerie Lane between the farms, while across the harbor were the great manor-houses of the patroons. The settlement was gay with flags and bunting, for the people were still celebrating the granting of a city charter.

"What a mixed people!" I remarked to Aboab as the city poured out its hundreds. "Every man different from his neighbor: gay Catholic from Spain, stolid Hollander, white-collared Puritan, English Cavalier, Irish peasant, quaint Quaker, blackamoors, Indians, and many others."

Aboab, ever timid, drew back at the sight. Remembering the hatred and bigotry of our fellow-passengers, he said, "Shall we really find friends in this new country, brother mine?"

"What did Manasseh say?" I replied, stifling my own grave fears.

Aboab smiled; Manasseh was his anchor. "Yes, we will find friends," he agreed, "and I have you."

"Would it were a better man," I began, feeling weak in the face of the great mystery ahead of us.

"Manasseh said you would be a tower of strength, and I believe him," said Aboab quietly.

A wave of resolution and courage swept over me at these simple words. I was ready to face lions, to go forth and conquer for God and Israel.

Then came on board three men. Peter Stuyvesant we recognized at once by the wooden peg, ornamented with silver bands, which did duty for the leg he had lost in the Company's service. With masterful spirit he strode down the deck. Pointing to us, conspicuous in our gabardines, the long, loose garment worn exclusively by our people for centuries, he said savagely to the shipmaster, "Jews! Who dared send them here? We want none such. They shall never land on this soil!" His face flamed and his voice roared above the creaking of the vessel and the noisy shouts of the sailors as they unloaded the cargo. One of the men with him, however, whose gay spirit contrasted vividly with that of the Governor, interrupted:

"Here, now, old spitfire," he shouted, giving the Governor such a resounding thump on his back that the angry man choked, spluttered, and perforce had to be silent. "Just what we need—a couple of Jews for the Catholics to burn ——"

"They won't burn!" roared Stuyvesant, failing to note the twinkling eyes. "These Jews are under my protection. Woe to him who touches a hair on their heads!"

"Well, have it your own way, then," said Van Rensselaer, the wealthiest man in the colony. "But they'll burn!"

"They won't!" snarled the Governor.

"They will!" replied the unruffled patroon.

At this moment a third man poured oil on the troubled waters. "Oh, give us peace!" he said, extending his hands in smiling protest. "You can write to the Company, Governor, on this matter."

"Umph!" was all the reply Stuyvesant made as he turned away.

Then this peacemaker came over to us, and to our surprise said, "Come with me."

Without a word, we left the ship and passed through the crowds. Many were the exclamations of hatred that reached our ears, but our new-found friend seemed not to hear them, and we humbly followed.

He took us to one of the houses near the windmill. Two kittens ran out, and a dog barked joyously, as he stopped to examine the autumn flowers in his window-boxes. Truly, this is a strange man, I thought. There are but a few in this savage age who descend to such humble things. Then he turned, gave us each a hand and bade us welcome. An old woman, with bent and twisted back, hobbling about on a stick, prepared a meal. Occasionally she glanced up at our friend with an eye—she had but one—of adoration. Seeing my look of puzzlement, he said: "That's Martha. She was to have been burnt as a witch; I—" but he lapsed into a day-dream and forgot us.

"I am Roger Williams," he said, after we had eaten. "We have founded a settlement in Rhode Island as a shelter for persons distressed for conscience and have named it Providence, in memory of God's merciful providence to us in our distress. As its first Governor, I went to England to request a charter from my friend Oliver Cromwell. Recently I met Manasseh ben Israel, whose desire was that I should look to your interests. To that end did he trust me to deliver this package to you."

Then did this man, whom we afterward came to know so well as the first grand advocate of liberty in these colonies, give us Manasseh's letter, in which he commended Roger Williams to us. Aboab opened the package and then fell a-weeping, for in the golden frame appeared the lifelike face of Manasseh, painted by his friend Rembrandt, that wonderful artist who lived in Amsterdam's Jewish quarter, and whose humanity and sympathy had transferred to canvas the speaking lips and brilliant eyes of the rabbi.

Now, the strange thing about all this was that Roger Williams, the gentile, wept with us, laughed with us and made us forget our troubles and danger.

Indeed, trials and tribulations did come upon us thick and fast. It was Governor Stuyvesant's desire to send us back to Holland, but while he was meditating on this matter, word came that the English from Long Island were about to attack, and every man was needed to help erect a wall from Coenties' Slip across the fields to the fort by the North River, and build the street to run alongside of it—the Wall Street.

We two Jews willingly joined in the work of carrying the posts to the site of the stockade; but, while I am strong and sinewy, poor Aboab, at first, could barely survive the day, and his cough grew worse. He improved in health, however, as the days went by, and we were given the work of filling swamps and marshes with rocks, stones, and fallen trees.

So useful did the Governor find us that he allowed the *Pear Tree* to sail away without us. From the windmill we watched its departure with mingled feelings.

We were not allowed to live within the settlement. A broken and weather-worn hut in the woods, where Indians once bartered furs for beads and where Peter Minuit in 1626 had bought Manhattan Island for sixty guilders, was allotted to us.

One evening, sitting on the rude bench outside this hut, which we had repaired to the best of our ability, we heard a low moan in the nearby thicket. Then, in the deepening shadows we saw the figure of a man crawling painfully toward us.

Hastening to his assistance, we saw with surprise that he was Samuel Drisius, the schoolmaster. A terrible wound in his shoulder was bleeding freely.

Without delay we carried him into the hut. Aboab removed a musket ball, stopped the flow of blood and dressed the wound.

Under his skilful attention, the schoolmaster recovered sufficiently to begin telling his story. He had proceeded so far as to explain that he had been searching the woods for certain herbs, as was his wont, being a man of strange notions—when, suddenly, he pointed to the door and shouted: "Indians! To the Governor, quick!" Then, as his wound broke out afresh, he fainted.

We quickly scented danger. After hasty consultation, Aboab agreed to remain with the dominie, while I hastened to the Governor. I sped over the rough and rocky woodland, falling over great stones, splashing through the many brooks and water courses, bruising myself greatly, but I covered the ground rapidly and reached the Governor's house. The door was open. I knocked and entered. Stuyvesant was half-reclining in a great chair, his wooden leg supported by a stool.

"Out on ye, Jew!" he exclaimed, starting up in anger and bringing his heavy fist down on the table. "What means this boorish intrusion?"

"Indians!" I gasped.

Then this extraordinary man became suddenly calm.

"Where?" he snapped, reaching for his sword.

I told him of the schoolmaster and the hut.

68

"Umph!" he growled, "serves him right for wandering too far from the settlement."

He snapped out orders on every hand. A bugle sounded; torches appeared; piles of dry brush blazed up and threw a glare over the scene; mounted guns from the Battery rumbled by, bumping over rocks and logs; musketeers fell into companies, and the Burgher Guard gathered from taverns, coffee-houses, and their homes. Stuyvesant was another man in this hour of danger. Stumping everywhere, he calmed the women and children and gave orders to the men. His masterful spirit instilled courageous confidence into the hearts of these people from every nation. He was now the man of the hour; all recognized his born leadership.

"Jew," he said, not unkindly, "guide these musketeers to the hut, and may God preserve ye! Go!"

The commander of the musketeers, Vincenta Fernandez, was a gentleman-adventurer of proud Spanish blood. No greater insult could have been given him than to order him to obey a Jew.

He flushed hotly. "*Sacre diablo!* Am I, a Catholic, to obey Judas?" he snarled.

The Governor turned to the second in command: "Here, put this fellow in the guardhouse and take charge yourself. We will attend to this Papist rebel at our leisure."

Then he turned to converse with Van Rensselaer, who had arrived with a company of his tenants.

The musketeers quickly covered the ground, but when within sight of the cabin, they hid behind trees—an advantageous habit which they adopted from the Indians themselves—while I went on to reconnoiter.

When I reached the clearing in front of our hut, Jacob Aboab was in the center of it. He was bartering with a score of naked and hideously painted savages, fighting against time, delaying their departure for the settlement, trusting that his fellow-Jew would stand by him in the day of trial, that I, Jacob Barsimson, would bring help.

He had already traded Rembrandt's little picture with the gilt frame which pleased the childish minds of the savages more than the precious painting itself. He had spent much time in demonstrating the mysterious telescope, hitherto unknown even to most white men, setting Indian against Indian bargaining for it; and he, the greatest bargainer of them all! He had traded the strangest string of beads the Indians had ever seen—a complete alphabet of Hebrew letters, cut in iron and strung on a cord, an heirloom from his ancestor Davinus, the printer. The schoolmaster's knife, knapsack, and watch were in the hands of the savages.

The Indians, engrossed in their bargaining, did not hear us until I stepped into the clearing. They turned, but before an attack could begin, five-and-twenty muskets were discharged into the air, making a most

He was bartering with the Indians.

terrifying noise. The savages, taken by surprise, slipped away like shadows to warn the main body that the white man was prepared. Aboab and I made a litter of boughs and carried the schoolmaster back to the city.

Owing to this little incident, we were looked upon with more favor. Van Rensselaer treated us kindly when the Governor was not in sight, and allowed us to live on his manor, Rensselaerwyck. Stuyvesant called us before the Council, where Aboab caused much amusement by his account of the bartering; even the Governor's mouth twitched.

Then he turned to me. "What's your business, Jew?" he commanded.

"I was fisherman, pilot and chart-maker in Amsterdam, your honor," I replied. "My ancestry dates back to Judah Cresques, teacher of navigation, maker of maps and nautical instruments."

"What! The great 'Map Jew'?" inquired a *schepen*, or magistrate.

"Yes, your honor," I replied.

"Well," said the Governor, "as the pirates are growing bolder, it is high time that our inlets and waterways, the depths of our harbor and rivers be charted. Let it be resolved, therefore, that you shall do this work."

Van Rensselaer then spoke: "In the name of these two Jews who have, by the gracious permission of God, been allowed to be of service to this community,

72

I apply for a land patent, that these men may have land for cultivation and pasturage, to be free of all charges for ten years, and thereafter subject only to a quit-rent of one-tenth of the produce, according to the terms of the director-general's charter."

At this, the Governor stormed, while the Council of nine men fiercely opposed him, declaring that they would appeal to Holland if he did not observe the terms of the charter.

At this moment, one of the burghers glanced out of the window, then jumped to his feet. "A ship, a ship!" he cried. The Council, in a body, hastened to the Battery. We went with them, as no man bade us stay.

It was a small vessel, from South America, and great was our joy when we discovered it brought us twenty-seven Jews, men, women, and children, Brazil's most prominent citizens, fleeing from the community of Recifé, invaded by the Portuguese.

The Governor almost suffered apoplexy; even the populace was sullen. The newcomers were held in the custody of the provost marshal. Their goods were sold on the Battery green by public auction, for, in their hasty flight, they had not had time to turn their property into ready money. The master of the ship imprisoned David Israel and Moses Ambrosius, until, out of the kindness of their hearts and to spite the Governor, certain burghers paid the passage money in full and settled the matter.

The Governor was so angry that he stepped up to Abraham de Lucena, their leader, seized him by his white beard and shouted, "None of the Jewish nation shall be permitted to infest New Netherland!" Then and there, he instructed his clerk to write the Company immediately.

As the crowds dispersed, Jacob Aboab and myself found an opportunity to speak to the despairing little group of Jews.

And here, dear reader of this poor account of those early days, I would call your attention to that wonderful event which shows the goodness of God to all His people. I had stepped over to a forlorn, weeping lady, sitting on one of the half-sunken posts of the wharf. Evidently a lady of wealth and culture, I thought, for her head-dress and skirt were of the finest lace and black satin. I spoke a word of cheer in Hebrew. With a startled look, she raised her head. "God of Israel, who are you?" she cried.

"Jacob Barsimson," I answered gently, "of your own people; I would ——"

But I got no further. With a cry of joy that brought the immigrants clustering around in wonder, she flung her arms around me. "My son, my son! Oh, my son!" was all she could say.

My bewilderment was complete. All I remembered of my childhood was the coming of a nameless horror, hidden from childish eyes by loving parents; weeping servants; the hasty flight; baby sister Ruth; the somber woods, hunger, thirst, misery, then lonesomeness in a cold, damp and foggy land among strangers far from sunny Spain. Manasseh thought my parents had been exiled for not paying the special poll tax of thirty pieces of silver levied on all Jews.

But my mother was speaking between happy sobs, while I, with open mouth and eyes half out of my head, was stricken dumb.

"Here is your father Isaac, and your sister Ruth. Oh, son, God is good to us!"

Then I found my senses. I kissed my mother, Ruth, and my father, again and again. We were wild with joy. I dragged Aboab into our family circle, and Father introduced Ephraim Suerio, brother-in-law of Manasseh, and other friends.

Our family had, indeed, been scattered. My father, after a short imprisonment, and exile, had roamed as far as England, while my mother wandered through France; Ruth had been taken to Brazil by her Jewish nurse; another faithful servant had left me in Holland.

Now we had all met on the Battery green of New Amsterdam never to part again.

The open air of America had made Jacob Aboab a new man. Gentle and refined, he was good to look upon. I think our bright-eyed Ruth thought so, too, judging by certain shy looks. Aboab, too, eyed her with reverence.

Happy as we were, however, our condition was precarious. The Council, for once, sided with the angry Governor. The Sheriff announced that every Jew must prepare to depart forthwith.

In our perplexity God sent Roger Williams to us. To our great delight, he restored our three treasures—the strung Hebrew alphabet, the telescope, and the picture. The Indians always were his friends, for he knew their language and sympathized with them.

When he left for his own beloved settlement, some of our people went with him, and God was good to them, we heard.

Several days passed. The darkest hour came. We stood by Coenties' Slip once again, our baggage in our hands, watching the arrival of the ship which would carry us all away. An agent of the Company was the first to land. He presented a letter from the directors to the Governor.

Stuyvesant read it; then, as he silently turned away, handed the document to Van Rensselaer. One glance, then his face brightened. He told us that the Governor had been severely rebuked and that a favorable decision had been given whereby we were to be allowed to carry on our business peacefully and to exercise in all quietness our religion.

Now, as I look back over the years and recall how we were permitted to hold land and become burghers, and how our people came in great numbers—as I remember Aboab printing the first book in his new office for the schoolmaster, my own great success as a mapmaker, Jacob's and Ruth's marriage by Isaac

Aboab, the first Jewish wedding by the first rabbi in North America before he returned to Holland, Stuyvesant's downfall and the coming of the English, who changed the name of our city to New York—as I recall all these things of the past and remember also that we have just erected our new synagogue on the street that runs by the windmill, I thank the Lord God of Israel that Jacob Aboab and I were found worthy of being pioneers of Israel.

How strange it seems! These Hebrews in their graves,
  Close by the street of this fair seaport town,
Silent beside the never-silent waves,
  At rest in all this moving up and down.
                              —LONGFELLOW.

DAVID ISRAEL, the Jewish peddler from New Amsterdam, leaned against the rail of split cedar that prevented cattle from wandering off the green of the
little Connecticut settlement of New Haven, and re-
garded with lack-luster eyes the agile prancing of a
fencing master, who was demonstrating on a small
platform to a broad-brimmed, conical-hatted crowd
of Puritans, his cleverness with the rapier.

Wearied, however, by the boastful words and actions of the swordsman, the young Jew turned his
back on the performance, taking care not to step on
the two bulky oilskin packs at his feet—his stock-in-

78

trade with the Indians. He rested his broad shoulders against a small tree in whose shade he stood and gave free rein to his gloomy thoughts.

So deep was his frown, so dejected the droop of his shoulders, and so hopeless an air did he have, that a stout, middle-aged Puritan minister, who was sauntering by with a young Indian attending him, turned and eyed him curiously.

"Why so sad, friend?" he asked. "The scowl on thy face wouldst stop the workings of a grandfather's clock, as my good dame would say." The keen eyes twinkled with unusual humor for a Puritan.

At the sound of the unexpected voice, David looked up. In the presence of the older man, he instinctively removed his hat.

"I—sir?" David hesitated for a moment. "Well, if the truth is wanted, I'm fair sick of life!" he said bitterly.

"Tut, tut! At the threshold of thy days—and tired of life!" exclaimed the Puritan with gentle raillery. "And thou a young man favored above all men!"

" 'Favored above all men,' " repeated David, puzzled.

"Art thou not a Jew?"

"Yes, sir. I am a Jew!" replied David simply, pride flushing his olive-hued cheeks.

"And one of God's chosen people, favored Israel!" added the stranger with a smile. "Then why art thou so sore distressed?"

"Because of that very fact, sir," said David, touched by the genuine sympathy of the man. "Bitter strife and ill-feeling seem to follow our people where'er we roam."

The Puritan's manner encouraged speech.

"The Holy Office drove my ancestors from Spain to Holland," continued David in a tense voice.

"Ill-feeling sent us to the Dutch colonies in South America. There our people courageously pioneered and heroically resisted the efforts of the cruel Portuguese to destroy the peaceful civilization built up by the Dutch.

"But it was in vain. Again we had to flee.

"Believing that our strong resistance to the common foe would procure a welcome for us in the Dutch city of New Amsterdam, we came, only to find ourselves spurned by Governor Stuyvesant and deprived of our lawful and civic rights as Dutch burghers.

"Captured by pirates but rescued by a French warship, we landed at the Battery pier without means. Our goods were sold, and, as an indignant spokesman of our little party, I was arrested and held until all the monies were paid.

"Trading with the savages for pelts, I was at first successful. But, for some unknown reason, the Indians became unfriendly, so Jacob Lucena and I came to New Haven."

The Puritan was deepy interested. "Yes," he said, "and then?"

"We found the Indians of Connecticut more difficult to trade with than those around New Amsterdam.
Life amid the New England snows became very dull
so Jacob and I, craving excitement and adventure,
forgot our troubles in gay company.

"Arrested at Jonathan Marsh's country tavern at
Milford, we were fined twenty shillings apiece and
ordered to leave the settlement before the end of the
year. The Council has passed a 'strangers' law that in
the future no citizen shall receive non-inhabitants
without the consent of a town-meeting.

"And our last Dutch stiver has already been spent,"
concluded David with a rueful smile.

"Thou sayest the Indians are unfriendly?" questioned the Puritan sharply.

"Yes, Reverend," replied David. "The Indians
traded freely at first; but now they are silent and
surly. It doesn't pay to visit their camps."

"Umph!" muttered his listener reflectively.

There was deep silence for several minutes. David
eyed the Puritan's Indian attendant curiously—a
young man of about twenty years of age, bright-eyed
and agile. He was clad in a short deerskin robe with
tight trousers of the same material reaching down to
his leather-moccasined feet. His attitude was respectful, and it was evident that his attachment to the Puritan was very sincere.

The silence was broken by the challenging cry of
the fencing master:

"Ye good and honorable citizens of ye fair city of New Haven," the capering man cried, waving his long, thin rapier. "Take notice, one and all, that, begging your honorable pardon, and meaning no offense, I herewith challenge any man, whether he be of ye town guard or not, to engage in lively combat with your 'umble servant, Sergeant-at-Arms 'Enery Purkus, late of London town. God save ye King!"

Both David and the Puritan turned and looked at the little scene.

Swish, swish, swish! The flashing steel sparkled like lightning in the rays of the setting sun.

"Any man; any weapon; any method of attack!" challenged the swordsman.

A sudden stir among the crowd of gaping Puritans and a stern-faced, eagle-eyed, young looking man with the bronzed cheeks and weather-worn attire of the veteran soldier, leaped at one bound to the platform.

"Here, sir!" he cried in a brisk, military voice. "I'll allow no such challenge to go past me!" He twisted his moustache defiantly and pulled at his little pointed beard. Then, with a sweep of his hand, his hat fell to the boards.

There was a gasp of astonishment.

"A Roundhead!" exclaimed the Reverend to David, as he saw a head shaved to the poll, glisten in the sunshine.

"Your weapon, sir?" inquired the sergeant tersely.

The Cromwellian ex-soldier clapped his hand to his side.

"Ods' body!" he growled. "I forgot!"

The stern faces of the Puritans softened. Their eyes twinkled with amused expectancy.

Somebody passed up a mop and a bucket in which was some dirty rain water.

From the opposite side of the platform a small Dutch cheese wrapped in a cloth was rolled across the planks.

The Roundhead laughed grimly. "On guard, then!" he cried, turning and facing the fencing master. "Here's my sword and buckler. Come on with your bird-spit!"

The puzzled sergeant decided to teach his mocking opponent a lesson. With a brilliant flourish he attacked.

A moment later his rapier was dexterously caught, twisted and entangled in the cloth-covered cheese, while the mop, wet and dirty, passed swiftly across his face and then around his neck.

The Puritans forgot their religion and laughed uproariously.

David, now interested, forgot his grievances and smiled.

The Puritan's eyes, however, were intently focused upon the nonchalant Roundhead.

Now the play was over. Sergeant Purkus, to save his face, relinquished his weapon, while his opponent, hands on hips, mockingly looked him up and down.

With a howl of rage, the sergeant snatched a couple of broadswords from the rack behind him.

"Halt!" cried the Roundhead.

His commanding voice created an immediate silence all over the green.

"Friend!" Ringingly clear was his voice. "I have been playing wi' ye. But, ods' body! If I have to fight wi' the sword, I'll surely kill ye!"

"The devil!" exclaimed Sergeant Purkus. "Ye must be General William Goffe! None other would defy me—the great ——"

Oliver Cromwell's favorite general nodded.

" 'Tis Goffe himself!" muttered the Puritan divine with sudden awe. "This is serious," he continued, turning to David. "He is one of the English exiles whom the new king's officers, sent from the old country, seek to arrest for signing the death warrant of King Charles the First.

"These regicides only appear from their hiding-places when there is great trouble threatening our people."

David nodded understandingly. He gazed with admiring eyes at the commanding figure who was now fraternizing with the milling crowd, not so loyal to King Charles the Second as they were expected to be.

"I am John Eliot," said the Puritan to David in a tone of sincere friendliness, "and by the grace of God, an apostle to the poor Indians, whom I deeply love."

84

He placed a hand fondly upon the shoulder of the immobile young servant. The innate kindliness and simplicity of the minister impressed David deeply.

"The Massachusetts Council, alarmed by the unrest among the Indian tribes, even as far north as the wilderness of Maine, has sent me to consult with the only man who thoroughly understands the mind of the savage and who can control it, Roger Williams.

"Now, let's climb yon hill and see—what we shall see!" he added cryptically.

Two miles inland from the village green rose the rocky spurs, several hundred feet high, known as the East and West Rocks.

To the West Rock, across the lumpy ground, John Eliot and David Israel, with the Indian youth, whom the Puritan called Joseph, made their way. David carried his packs strung on cords passing over his shoulders.

The middle-aged minister was somewhat stout so the younger men kept their pace to suit that of their leader. John Eliot was the first to come out upon the summit of the hill from behind a thick patch of wild laurel. He scanned the horizon with anxious eyes.

Then he groaned aloud.

From all the peaks of the distant hills thin wisps of smoke could be faintly seen, rising almost perpendicularly in the still air. A dull, ruddy brown tinged the rays of the setting sun. The minister wiped his perspiring brow with a huge handkerchief.

"There's grave trouble brewing. Our peril is far greater than I thought," he muttered. "O God! Protect our helpless people!" The fervency of his voice thrilled David.

John Eliot suddenly clutched David's arm. His eyes blazed. "I see it now!" he cried. "From Maine to the Delaware the savages in many thousands are massing. Some sinister influence, born of the Devil himself, is moving upon their darkened minds for the purpose of combining the tribes into a confederacy to frustrate the will of God in these colonies."

David nodded understandingly.

"There's not a moment to lose!" David winced at the Puritan's grip on his arm. "There's only one man in all New England who can halt the murderous plan of the savages—Roger Williams!"

Again David nodded.

"And he is visiting friends at Hartford, thirty-five miles due west of this hill, and between us," John Eliot's long arm waved from north to south, "the savages are swarming like hordes of angry wasps. And you and I alone know the terrible truth!"

David looked thoughtful; then his face momentarily paled at the awful prospect.

"Thou hast a young man's desire for adventure," the Puritan was speaking very slowly and deliberately now. "Over yonder," pointing toward the setting sun, "Roger Williams awaits the coming of a messenger. Wilt thou be that messenger?"

86

David's mind was in a turmoil. The Puritan was still speaking, pleadingly: "The safety of many thousands of innocent souls depends on the messenger's courage, wisdom, and speed. Wilt thou go?"

"But, sir," said David, "while the venture is one after my own heart, I cannot but reason why I should imperil my life on behalf of ungrateful gentiles, the intolerant Stuyvesant, the—saving your pardon and presence, sir—harsh, unkind Puritans of the North who have fined, imprisoned, and driven us away from their settlements? Indeed, we Jews have often found the savages far more tolerant and kind than the Christians themselves."

John Eliot nodded understandingly. "I know," he murmured, placing a friendly hand on David's shoulder. "But dost recall that Cromwellian republican soldier? General Goffe and his comrades are hunted through the colonies, a price upon their heads, the king's officers seeking to deport them to England for execution. Hiding in caves, exiled from their families, suffering want and privation year after year, these men, who controlled England for ten years, come out into the open in the hour of danger to give their lives, if need be, for the safety of our honest settlers and their wives and children."

"I, too, would defend the forts, even as we did in Surinam if the savages attacked," said David.

John Eliot continued speaking as though he heard not.

"And Roger Williams, whom I would have you find—that noble, yet gentle soul—was driven away from his home and family by the Massachusetts Council for the crime of saying that the English king had no right to give the lands and heritage of the Indians away without payment of a purchase price to them.

"For several weeks he wandered amid the deep snows of a cruel winter until he found safety among the savages who welcomed him gladly. He, too, I know, will forgive his enemies, leave the safety of well-guarded Hartford and risk everything in order to aid the people of Massachusetts who have sent me to find him."

David, though deeply moved, still remained silent.

"And wilt thou—a son of Israel—refuse to ——"

"I'll go, sir! I'll go! Come what will, I'll find the Governor of Rhode Island and give him your message."

"See! I knew thy soul! Thou knowest the Indian trails through the wilderness and the river path. With thy youth and wisdom thou canst overcome all difficulties and dangers and reach Hartford quicker than any other man. Joseph shall go with thee as thy companion. May the God of thy fathers be with thee every step of the way!" He held out a friendly right hand. David gripped it with genuine fervor.

David, clad in a trapper's outfit he had recently purchased from a man at Fort Orange, was well prepared for the journey through the woods, and after this somewhat informal blessing of his new friend, he stopped only to hide his traveling packs in one of the clefts of a nearby cave, and then, with Joseph by his side, plunged immediately into the gloomy primeval forest that came down to the very edge of the settlement.

Following a charcoal-burner's rough-log road until they came to a winding path that led by the edge of the beaver swamps, they continued traveling upon it until an opportunity arose of branching off on to an Indian trail that led down to the Quinnipiac River.

"There's an old Indian fisherman who lives by himself in a cavern by the falls," said David. "Perhaps we can learn something from him; he was always well-disposed."

"Old Squantum?" said Joseph, his voice soft and musical.

"That's the man!" answered David. "I hear the falls already."

Within a few minutes they were at the heap of stones piled up outside the cave and at their call an old, wrinkle-faced Indian shuffled out.

He scowled deeply when he saw the youths and with a muttered "Ugh!" turned and disappeared into the depths of his cavern again.

In spite of their calls, he refused to reappear.

"What shall we do?" inquired Joseph.

"Can't make Indians talk if they don't want to," remarked David, "and we've no time to waste. Let's follow the river. A few miles farther on there's another old Indian fisherman who also lives by himself. He chattered like a Surinam parrakeet the last time we met. Perhaps he'll be more communicative than Squantum."

Through the darkening woods, guided by the rapidly-flowing stream, the youths hurried. As they strode deeper and deeper into the primeval forest, following the narrow Indian trails, an oppressive spirit of hostility and danger appeared to hover over them, causing them to walk more carefully and to glance covertly around as though they expected to be attacked.

A startled deer crashing through the undergrowth caused them to fall flat on the ground behind the huge trunk of a fallen tree.

Laughing at their fears, however, they pressed on.

About an hour later David and his companion reached the clearing where "Charley," the second Indian fisherman had his nets spread out to dry. They found him sitting by the side of a small fire, near a skin-covered rock-shelter.

A scowl settled upon the imperturbable face of the old Indian.

He met their friendly greetings with a grunt, and to their inquiries regarding Indian affairs he was non-committal.

David gave the Indian a packet of fish-hooks as a gift.

"We're on our way to Hartford," David explained, "and ——"

"Go back, White Youth!" exclaimed the Indian suddenly, looking up from the hooks in the palm of his hand. "I friend—but speak not. Go back to Quinnipiac!" he said, using the Indian name for New Haven.

"No! We're going on to Hartford," said David stubbornly.

The old Indian slowly handed the hooks back to David.

"No want un," he grunted.

"Why?"

"You no believe," grunted old Charley with an ugly scowl. "I friend—save you! Over there," he rose and pointed to the West, "danger, torture, death!"

"Why?"

Old Charley bent his head and hoarsely whispered in David's ear two words, "Philip! Hiawatha!"

For one brief moment David's face blanched, his heart beat wildly. "King Philip," the sachem of the Pequots, was the vindictive, organizing genius of the Indians, ever planning a united effort by all the tribes to exterminate the hated whites. "Hiawatha" was the legendary chief of all the divisions of the Iroquois tribes; his unseen spirit was the rallying-point.

"Go back!" urged the Indian. "I, good friend, tell you!" He spoke to Joseph, quick, sharp words in the

Indian language, and the youth interpreted them to David: "Mohegans, seven hundred strong, naked, oiled and war-painted, are crossing the rivers everywhere. He advises us to go back immediately."

"No. We will go on!" said David determinedly.

"Ugh! Fool!" grunted the Indian and, suddenly turning, stamped angrily into his shelter.

The sun had set and the light was fading fast. But knowing well the route they must travel, the young men stealthily picked their way along the almost invisible trail in a line due west, keeping the river on their right.

For more than two hours they tramped the silent woods, ever on the watch for the faintest signs of hostile Indians. Several times they were alarmed by sounds and movements in the forest—the wind among the trees, the restless wild life, and even by the swirling, rippling waters of the forest brooks and streams—but they encountered nothing, although they had an uncomfortable feeling of being followed and watched by unseen eyes.

By the time the moon was well up they had reached the Hanging Hills of Meriden, a score of miles on their journey, where ridges of trap rock terminate at Chestnut Hill. On its summit they found remains of Indian signal fires—the green boughs still giving off a pungent smoke.

"Four fires in a group—that means, 'Come to the Council,'" explained Joseph.

David nodded. "But the Indians have left," he said. "They're on their way."

"Look!" cried Joseph. "Over there!"

To their left a dim red glow amid clouds of dark smoke hanging over the trees denoted Indian activity. But there was no sound.

"The silence of the Indians is more impressive than their war-whoops!" remarked David. "I can see camp-fire smoke in every direction, and though they are quiet, we must be in their midst now. It'll take all our wits to get through. Here we leave the Quinnipiac River and strike across to the Connecticut River, following it to Hartford."

While talking they had picked their way down the steep hillside and again they followed, more cautiously than ever, the Indian trails.

They continued silently on their way, avoiding all evidences of Indian camping parties. The forest was now as silent as the hot night itself. Save for the fitful sparkle of an occasional camp-fire, they might have been the only travelers in the forest.

And then without warning, they stumbled on to a long file of silently marching men. With an instinctive cry of alarm, David fell back, but too late.

He was seized by the man nearest to him; but, to his surprise, it was a white man.

Explanations followed. The marching men proved to be Captain Robert Treat and a party of settlers traveling from Milford to Newark, New Jersey.

Treat had, of course, noticed the activity of the Indians, and thinking that the savages were planning an attack on their camp, the white men were quietly marching in Indian file away from the dangerous locality.

When David explained the full meaning of the Indians' activity, Robert Treat decided to turn and go back to the defense of New Haven.

Bidding a friendly, though silent adieu to the men from Milford, David and his companion hurried on, making the best speed possible, until they reached the Connecticut River, where they halted for a brief breathing spell.

Then, following in many places the river course, skirting the high brown stone hills and passing through the narrows, they suddenly came upon a terrible scene—the still smoldering ruins of a settler's home.

In the trampled corn and potato patch at its rear were the scalped and murdered settler and his little family, their labors forever at an end.

With senses numbed by the horrible scene as revealed by the ghostly light of the moon, David and his companion took to the now welcome woodland trail again.

Within a few hundred yards of the scene of the massacre, they turned aside to avoid the Indian village of Mattabesett.

As they prepared to break into the uncharted wilderness David noticed a figure in black tied to a stake at one side of the sleeping settlement.

Clutching his companion's arm, he whispered, "Look! There's a captive! We must find out whether— Merciful Heavens! It's a Catholic mission father! And he's been tortured by the savages. See, the ashes at his feet are still smoldering!"

Only for a moment did David hesitate. Then, "We'll save him!" he whispered in Joseph's ear. "I have a plan. John Eliot spoke of the Indians being remnants of our lost ten tribes. I'll be an Indian."

Stripping off his leather jacket and tearing his shirt wide open at the neck, he searched until he found some plants of the pokeweed species. Crushing them in his hands, he quickly stained his face, neck and chest a light purple.

In the moonlight and in the uncertain, flickering firelight, with his closely cropped hair, his slightly aquiline nose, his oval face and dark skin, he appeared sufficiently horrible to pass for an Indian, if one did not look too closely.

Then slowly crawling into the open and closely watching the nearest Indian sentry, he finally reached the poor victim of Indian savagery.

David caught his breath as a nearby campfire flickered into a momentary blaze. But the Indians were keeping a very careless watch. The martyr, a small, wiry man, was almost unconscious and did not appear to realize that deliverance was at hand.

Noticing that the Indian sentry was nodding sleepily, David, with a slash of his hunting-knife, cut the prisoner's cords and as the little man fell forward, caught him in his arms.

The athletic young Jew, picking him up like a child, swiftly carried him into the woods.

To his relief there was no outcry.

"To the river, Joseph," he whispered. "Quick! There are probably canoes drawn up at the water's edge. He cannot walk. We must, therefore, paddle up to Hartford. It will take longer, against the stream, but it will save a human life." He looked with pity at the diminutive priest, so thin and weak with privation and torture.

"The savages have brought him far," muttered David. "From the Huron country, probably. But we'll save him from their cruel grasp."

To their satisfaction, they discovered several canoes drawn up under trees at the water's edge.

Selecting one suitable for their purpose and laying the cruelly-tortured man carefully in its cradle-like center, they sent the canoe spinning out into the stream and then paddled vigorously toward Hartford.

Drawing in close to the sheltering darkness of the overhanging trees, whenever they saw evidence of Indians on the banks, they soon found themselves nearing their destination.

Rounding a bend of the river, a "hello" came across the water from the bank.

With a sharp cry to Joseph to paddle harder, David raced the canoe over the water like a flying fish.

Joseph, however, stopped.

"White man!" he explained.

Again the hail, "Ahoy there!"

Carefully guiding the canoe to shore, David searched the bank. A tall white man, dressed in Puritan garb stood awaiting them.

"Art thou Indian or white?" asked the stranger in a calm, clear voice.

"We're both!" replied David. Sudden relief as he noticed the manly poise of the Puritan minister caused him to speak facetiously. "I'm Indian, Jew, and white man all rolled into one, sir! And I have a message for the Reverend Roger Williams from his friend John Eliot of New Haven."

"I am the man ye seek!" In his eagerness the Governor of Rhode Island strode knee-deep into the river to meet the canoe.

"And this is Joseph, John Eliot's Indian servant, sir," continued David, at the same time handing the sealed packet he had brought with him to the Puritan. " 'Tis fortunate that we met you, sir."

" 'Tis providential! What is the message that required such speed?" inquired Roger Williams.

David quickly outlined the wide scope of Indian discontent.

Roger Williams' calm, strong face became very grave. "My soul was oppressed with the fear that some grave disturbance was agitating the tribes," he said, "and so I came out to investigate. 'Tis the guidance of Providence that I should meet thee. But whom have you there?" He clicked his tongue and drew back in horror as he saw the torn, mutilated fingers and hands and the twisted, burnt limbs of the black-robed priest.

David narrated the events of their journey as Roger Williams listened sympathetically.

"Ye have done well, faithful servants!" he said, shaking hands with them in his admiration of their courage. "But we must get this poor man to Hartford. He needs assistance badly. Then I will go to the Indian encampments and try to halt this threatening bloodshed. So help me, God!" he added, removing his broad-brimmed hat, reverently.

At that moment the missionary priest, stirring fitfully, awoke and looked around with wondering eyes. "Where am I?" he asked.

"With friends," said David gently, and briefly explained the situation to him.

"And how soon can I go back to my poor Indians?" asked the missionary.

"What zeal! What sacrifice! What love!" exclaimed Roger Williams looking curiously at the seldom seen figure of a Catholic mission father in New England.

"Umph!" snorted David angrily. "For this terrible cruelty alone the savages deserve extermination!"

Roger Williams shook his head. "No, friend. Thou

art wrong. Not extermination, but civilization and education. I would see them living in peace with the white man, in communities built according to the plan laid down in thy Hebrew Scriptures of old. But, come! We will go at once to Hartford."

Then Roger Williams showed that he was practical as well as visionary. He took charge of everything. Then he sought out the Indians.

❋   ❋   ❋

"Brothers!" It was "King Philip," the great chief, who was speaking. "You see this vast country which the Great Spirit gave to our fathers and to us. Brothers, these palefaces from the unknown world are destroying our groves, spoiling our hunting and planting grounds, and are driving us and our children from the graves of our fathers and our Council fires. The spirit of Hiawatha is with us, and ——"

At this moment there entered into the Council hut of the Pequots, Mohegans, Iroquois, Narragansetts, and other Indian sachems, the well-beloved Governor of Rhode Island, Roger Williams. He bore in his hands the calumet of peace, its bowl of soft red stone, its reed ornamented with feathers.

There was a sudden dramatic, thrilling silence. Angry looks slowly disappeared from the faces of Nature's children as, puffing a whiff of its grayish smoke, Roger Williams gravely passed the peace-pipe around the Council circle.

99

Thus, hour by hour, did the bravest man of all New England battle calmly and intelligently against primitive vengeance and seek to keep the peace between white man and red.

Outside the crude hut many thousands of war-painted savages on hilltops and in the valleys awaited the final word of peace or war.

And peace won. The threatened war of extermination was averted, and for many years New England remained a smiling land.

John Eliot, the apostle to the Indians, with his ideal of government based upon the laws of the ancient Jewish state, continued his noble work of raising communities of "praying" Indians.

"And thou, my Jewish friend," said Roger Williams to David, when they again met, "wilt soon find the Indians willing to trade in peace and friendship, if such be thy plans. But shouldst thou or thy Jewish friends ever be persecuted for conscience sake, come thou to Providence, Rhode Island, where thou wilt find a welcome."

"I thank you, sir," replied David. "I would that I could go back to New Amsterdam—there's a certain Jewish maid. But, alas! That stiff-necked Dutch governor ——!"

"New Amsterdam has become English," said Roger Williams with a smile. "News has just arrived telling us of its downfall."

"Then I leave Connecticut at once, sir."

> "Then redmen took the law of love
>   As from a brother's hand,
>   And they blessed him while he founded
>   The city of our love."
> —*Old Philadelphia Ballad*

THE bells of London are ringing. 'Tis the early morning of the coronation day of James, the King. Within the banqueting hall of Westminster Palace, Master Dolland is making last-minute repairs on a great chandelier, while I, Jonas Aaron, his young assistant, watch with admiring eyes as deft fingers weave golden wire and sparkling crystal.

"The King!" he hoarsely whispers. "Down on your knees, knave!" We kneel in silent honor as two men enter the room.

"Oh, la, la!" merrily laughs he who is to be crowned, "and so, Friend Penn, thou thinkest thy savages are

101

lost remnants of the Jewish race, to be restored by
Quaker peace and good will. Methinks a regiment of
my guards ——"

"Friend," interrupts the other, "it doth please thee
to laugh at my holy experiment; but if thou hadst
seen the Jewish countenances of the Indian chiefs and
the beady black eyes of their children when they
came to the great parley on De la Warre's river, thou
wouldst have imagined thyself in Dukes' Place or
Berry Street, in the Jewish heart of this, thine own
royal city. Now, an Act of Toleration for ——"

"You shall have it, Governor Penn, for I, too, have
suffered for opinion's sake."

As I knelt there in a corner of that magnificent hall,
and overheard the conversation of King and Quaker,
my curiosity and interest were aroused. "Berry
Street" was the foul alley in which I lived—a filthy, rat-
infested, fog-laden slum of old-time London. Suddenly I saw the New World beckoning to me.

The Quakers, as their leader had said, were fully
convinced that the American Indians were the remnants of the lost ten tribes of Israel. By using this idea
as a method of approach I succeeded in interesting
Master James Logan, Governor Penn's secretary,
in my welfare.

So it came to pass that I found myself on the
Welcome with William Penn, carrying to Philadelphia its new charter.

Shall I ever forget that voyage—the escape from

the *Turk*, the contrary winds and storms which drove us from our course! In those three months we hungered and thirsted, and the plague visited us. The haughty Lord Peterborough stirred up mutiny, even the women of Penn's household murmured against him, and the only sign of the guidance of Providence was the birth of a sweet babe, whom we named Sea-Mercy.

I can still see the gentle, serious face and the far-away look that was ever in the eyes of Penn as he walked the narrow deck, praying for patience and a happy end to the voyage.

On a clear October Sabbath, in the year 1699, we first sighted the great city of two thousand houses, nestling in its sylvan beauty. The precipitous riverbank was lined with joyous crowds, while bedecked sloops and schooners fired salutes. The savages swarmed around us in their canoes and cried *"Issimus!"* (Brother). Others, swimming from the shore, climbed over our bows, and kneeling before the drab-clothed, beaver-hatted Governor, whose sole adornment was a blue network sash of silk, they offered him the good, brown earth of their native land. We were deeply touched as he passionately kissed its birch-bark wrappings; his lips moving in prayer.

Water-men drove their wherries past our ship and mingled their welcoming cries with those of the lumbermen on the log floats coming down the stream. On shore the Negroes were shouting, and the city's bells were pealing with joy. My heart was pounding with joy also. "Berry Street" with its sulphurous fog was no more. Before me stretched a clean, bright new city—my future home!

" 'Tis a brave and goodly city, Jonas," remarked James Logan, placing a friendly hand upon my shoulder, "and, indeed, thou art favored in being one of the first of thy race to settle in this holy spot, the land of thy forefathers, perhaps!"

I knew to what he referred, for being a scholar well versed in Hebrew and in the Bible, he had spent many an idle hour on the sea in discourse upon the scattering of our lost tribes to the end that this land should, in the wisdom of God, be settled by men of religious ideals.

We landed at the sign of Ye Blue Anchor Inn, where Master Shippen, the Mayor, a tortured, refugee Quaker from Massachusetts, the Governors of New York and New Jersey, and other notables, awaited the renowned William Penn.

James Logan had urged me to secure quarters at the tavern on the corner of Third and Chestnut Streets. I found it to be a large, unpainted wooden structure, old, even for those times. It was rapidly falling into decay, a true counterpart of its rusty, creaking sign, that of two crossed keys. Israel Israel, a strange old man, was its keeper.

Pushing open the door under the great, swinging sign, I entered its main room. This building was probably one of the old log houses of the sons of Sweden, I thought, as I noticed the loopholes for muskets in its sturdy walls. Rough furniture filled the room, and in the very spacious fireplace a little spit-dog, running in a revolving wire cylinder on the far side of it, was turning a venison roast.

Doors leading out of the main hall were barred and in spite of my knocks and cries, there was no reply, until, at the sudden darkening of the street door, I turned and saw a little, twisted, white-bearded figure, hideously scarred, bent and lame with infirmity or age. I knew from James Logan's description that this was my host.

He must have been more surprised than I, for he turned as though to flee, but changed his mind and entered. Removing his broad-brimmed Quaker hat, he said in a strange, thin voice, "Thee knowest this be Ye Crossed Keys Tavern?"

"Yes," I replied. "Friend Logan directed me here."

Hearing that name, he recovered his composure. "All's well," he muttered, rubbing his thin hands. "Friend Logan is indeed a godly man. Thy name?"

"Aaron—Jonas Aaron," I replied simply.

Although his back was turned as he was about to prepare pop-robbins and hominy at the fire, I saw him start and stumble, but before I could reach him he had recovered.

He released the little bow-legged prisoner, and we watched the tiny spit-dog dash down the street.

"See!" the old man cackled with glee. "He, too, loves liberty!"

"Art thou a Jew?" He turned with such sudden fierceness that a wave of fear swept over me.

"I am."

"Then beware!" He shook his head. "The masked clans are planning to oust the Quakers, and if it be known that thou art a Jew, thy life might even be imperiled."

"But," I queried, bewildered, "the Governor has just arrived and is this not what men call 'the city of brotherly love'?"

The queer little man snickered as he tapped the middle button of my coat with a long, claw-like finger. "Listen, thou stranger," he said, "thou knowest not the inner travail of this city of brotherly love."

"That is very true," I willingly admitted.

"Well, then; knowest thou that William Penn, godly man though he be, has many enemies who seek his ruin and the suppression of the goodly influence and power of his Quakers?"

"But why?" I asked. "I thought that all men loved so kindly a man as the Governor."

"Ah, ah!" The old tavern-keeper waved a crooked forefinger. "But certain wicked men seek power for their own evil ends," he cried. "The Deputy-Governor is bitterly envious of William Penn's greatness; Judge Quarry seeks political control of the colony on behalf of the idle, dissolute, and thieving rich. Willie

Penn, the Governor's young son, is the leader of the hard-drinking, noisy, and riotous clans that encourage the criminal elements, living in the river-bank caves of the first settlers, to further lawlessness. Ah, 'tis a troublous town thou hast come to, lad!"

I began to understand that all was not well in this Quaker city of brotherly love.

Israel Israel, who had stopped for breath, now continued, "These men, and others of like mind, seek to ruin the colony by taking advantage of our many troubles—our factional strife, the scarcity of money, the raging yellow fever, and the fact that the pirates are taking advantage of Quaker pacifism. Even the Indians are becoming restless under the treatment accorded them by certain white men."

Then a strange thing happened. The old man had worked himself up into a frenzy over the troubles of the colony, and now his mind began to wander and his speech to thicken. In the midst of a wild tirade, he stopped and looked at me with staring, frightened eyes. "And thou art a Jew!" he mumbled. "Ah, they come!" he suddenly cried. "They come! They come! But the crossed keys will save me!"

I sought to calm him, wondering at the same time what his mysterious outburst might mean. He gradually quieted down, and when other guests came in a little later the old tavern-keeper regained his normal manner as he attended to routine matters. From that time, however, he generally avoided me.

I confided the matter to Logan, who had indeed proved a true friend, introducing me to the private school of Anthony Benezet, on Chestnut Street, where I gave occasional lessons in Hebrew. He also obtained for me the work of riveting, with tiny diamond drills and gold thread, the delicate china and glassware that had been broken in the rough sea voyages.

To my inquiry he replied, "Israel Israel, the tavern-keeper, is a strange man, but he is apparently a good Quaker. He always attends our quiet meetings and sits and meditates, and conducts himself as a true Friend. Yet we know not his history and he liketh not to be questioned. We know, however, that he hath some secret fear or sorrow on his mind, a terror that comes to the surface when he is troubled and expresses itself in his references to the crossed keys, the name he gave to his tavern."

Time flew on and life in the New World was, on the whole, very pleasant—the fairs, the busy markets, the new arrivals, among them others of my people, who went to the surrounding settlements and traded with the Indians. Master Bradford, the printer, arrived with his printing-press, which he set up that he might issue a gazette.

Then, to my surprise and dismay, Governor William Penn suddenly left his beloved colony, never to return. His London agent, Philip Ford, had defrauded him of certain monies. The Governor was left penniless and spent some time in London's debtors' prison.

The tavern-keeper grew more and more morose, treating everybody with suspicion and fear. Whenever he saw me he would wag his hoary white head sadly. "They are coming!" he cried one morning. "I know it; I feel it! They will bring the torture irons, but the crossed keys over my door will save me."

I paid little attention to his words, putting them down as the vapid wanderings of an unbalanced mind. Yet that very evening the masked riders of the clans dashed through the streets with fiery torches, uttering his words: "They come! They come! Arise and defend your homes!"

The brave Swedes and Hollanders hurried to their old fort-like cabins with guns in their hands. The stolid Germans placed themselves under their pastor's leadership and hastily barricaded themselves and prepared to fight, but the unarmed Quakers gathered in their great meeting-houses and, silent as night itself, awaited the Spirit's guidance.

I was standing on Chestnut Street near the entrance of the Crossed Keys Tavern, when I saw John Churchman, the leader of the Quakers, seize the bridle of a passing rider. The powerful jerk unmasked the clansman. "Wilt thou halt, friend," the Quaker asked, "and tell us what the danger is?"

The Deputy-Governor, for it was he, bent low over the saddle and hissed, " 'Tis the French! Twelve of their cursed warships are coming up the Delaware!"

"Then thee hadst better get to thy quarters, John

Evans. We will make bandages for thee and thine when the fighting starts," remarked the Quaker dryly.

Other riders arrived. "Will you Quakers not fight?" one inquired.

"Our trust is in the arm of the Lord, the great Watchman of Israel!" cried John Churchman, as he strode off to meet his Quaker friends.

I stepped back into the shadow of the nearest doorway, for I was afraid of the rowdy clansmen.

At that moment a horseman rode up, and with a foul oath tore off his mask. It was Judge Quarry.

"Our plan of a false alarm has failed!" I heard him snarl to his fellow clansmen. "We may as well go to our homes. These Quakers have failed to rebel against their pacifist leaders, even when told that their homes and lives were in danger."

I realized then the full meaning of the clansmen's plot in spreading an alarm that an attack by French warships was imminent. The leaders of the Quakers, always opposed to the use of force, would not fight, and thus would be discredited, while the clansmen, with a big show of militant courage, would become the natural leaders of the other elements of the cosmopolitan population.

The plot had failed, however, and the clansmen dispersed. But the evil was done. Sudden panic seemed to have swept the city. Women and children wept, while the men boarded up their houses and prepared to defend them against the threatened attack.

Others threw their jewels and valuables into disused wells, and by boats and rafts sought refuge in the many creeks and waterways.

At the Crossed Keys Tavern strange things were happening. The old tavern-keeper and I had been watching with ever-increasing excitement the shouting mobs of men and boys marching toward the market-place with their heavy clubs, muskets and ancient blunderbusses. The light of madness was slowly kindling in Israel Israel's eyes. "They come! They come!" he shouted after them, "but the keys, the crossed keys will save me!" He pointed to his sign overhead and chuckled horribly.

Then he slowly turned, mumbling and muttering as he passed me. He tottered from room to room, supporting himself with his great gold-headed stick, and babbled almost incoherent words to the guests. Out of mere curiosity I followed him until he stopped at a door on the third floor. From within came the sound of droning Latin. He paused, staggered; then, with a scream of frightful intensity, he flung open the door with a crash.

Within I saw Irish Elizabeth McGawly, also De la Noe, the little French dude, and Bobby Fox, the simpleton, and others. Standing in front of a proscribed Papist altar was Michael Brown, the wine merchant's agent, now revealed as a Catholic priest. The Catholic practice of the Mass was forbidden in William Penn's colony.

The dapper little Frenchman stepped out and halted the intruder, but was felled by a blow from Israel's heavy stick. Then, dropping the cane, Israel drew a long and murderous-looking stiletto of Italian make.

The answer came to me like a flash of light. Israel Israel was a Jew with so fierce a secret hatred against the Catholic Inquisition that it had undermined his reason.

Pushing the women out of his way, he screamed at the priest, standing calmly by the altar of his fathers, "The Mass, thou Papist! That which I was forced to witness in thy Roman Vatican. This thou doest in my inn secretly. I'll denounce you; then what can save you from punishment? The French are upon us; they, too, are Catholic, and our people are mad with rage!"

"I am ready to answer for all my actions," said the priest with an air of sorrowful resignation as Israel faced him.

I stepped into the room and sought to restrain the frantic man, but Father Brown waved me back with a calm smile. It seemed to goad Israel almost beyond control.

"Priest!" he shrieked, "I was a Jew of Italy. Your people didst bend my neck, but not my spirit, for I mocked them. So thy Inquisitors, with this very blade I stole, clipped my ears and slit my nose and tongue. To break my spirit, they broke my body and tore my flesh, and didst teach that their Church could reach me wherever I fled. They have made me live in a hell of hate and fear, while I lived the Quakers' shadowy imitation of old-time Israel. Now thou hast come to torment me; but the keys, the keys over my tavern door, will save me." His thin voice trailed away in weakness, and I wept out of sheer pity for the man.

I expected to see the priest disarm the weak old man, but he did not. Beads of perspiration stood on Father Brown's marble-hued brow, his face was ashy pale, but not with fear.

With one swift movement he bared his breast. "Oh, son of Israel, stab me, then, if thou dost think it will give you peace. See, I await! Strike!"

Israel suddenly raised the gleaming stiletto. It was too late to stop him. The light of martyrdom shone in the good priest's eyes as he looked up and fingered his rosary, murmuring a prayer. Then, as Israel strangely hesitated, Father Brown murmured reflectively: "Now I understand fully what Friend Penn meant when he spoke of your fears and hates. I am ready. Come!"

Catholic and Jew were facing each other in the New World.

"But the cruel persecution of thy Church?" questioned Israel.

"The Church cannot err," said the priest proudly; "but we—oh, we sin grievously! As Faber, my bishop, so wonderfully says:

The troubled soul found rest at last.

" 'But we make our Father's love too narrow
  By false limits of our own,
  And we magnify His strictness
  With a zeal He will not own.' "

Israel's feeble frame bowed and shook with sobs.
Then, as Michael Brown caught him as he fell, the
old Jew raised his head for a moment and muttered,
"I, too, have sinned, for I would have broken the Law
of Moses, 'Thou shalt not kill!' "

We carried him to his room, and the troubled soul
found rest at last, with his eyes fixed on me and
his hand in mine, his fellow Jew, while Quaker John
Churchman, who had come in answer to my plea,
and the Papist priest stood by in solemn silence.

"He was a good Quaker," remarked John Churchman softly.

"Indeed, I believe he was a good man," assented
the priest with a sigh.

I asked Father Brown before I left the room if he
knew what Israel meant by his constant repetition
of "the crossed keys."

A look of ineffable sadness appeared on the face
of the priest as he explained, "The crossed keys of
Heaven are the Papal arms. In his early youth he was
probably told that this sign would save him from
the wrath of the Inquisition.

"Evidently frightful memories of the past, and in-
creasing terror of again falling into the hands of his
enemies, caused the idea of the protection of the

Papal keys to become a fixture in his feeble mind. He could not realize that in this New World, in this city of brotherly love, he was safe, and so, when he heard that the French were coming to attack us, bringing with them their Catholic religion, his reason collapsed entirely.

"His discovery of my hastily gathered harmless little congregation, and my humble self, finished this tragedy of the past—a past that we hope is forever gone."

"BRAVO! Heel over toe! Keep it up! Hooray!" Tom Bainbridge and the woman he called "missus" were celebrating. Their recent purchase of the wardenship of London's great prison in 1732 had proved very profitable.

Then the door flew open and a man in military garb entered, followed by two civilians.

"Who are you? Wot's matter? How'd ye get in?" spluttered the befuddled official of the Fleet prison.

"The King's business," the soldier curtly replied. "I am General Oglethorpe of the Life Guards. Reports of your evil doings have reached the King's ears. We are a commission sent to inquire into the state of his Majesty's prisons."

"Dost inquire into the riots of the debtors, my lord and gentlemen?" The jailer cringed before the great warrior. "'Tis not my fault, so may it please your honor. 'Twas all on account of a stiff-necked Jew refusing to take turn in begging."

"Lead the way, warden! We'll see for ourselves." Ignoring the alarmed official's efforts to delay investigation, Oglethorpe, followed by his friends, strode down the gloomy passages, where smoky lanterns revealed filth and vermin on every side.

The group entered a sixteen-foot cell, whose bare stone walls reflected the chills of death. Forty or fifty people were huddled together in common misery, while in a cage-like space, projecting over the street level, a crouched figure, with a rusty tin, cried to the passers-by, "Remember the poor debtors—a crust, a coin!"

"Let me see the Jew who refused to beg," demanded the General.

The warden, viciously kicking those within reach, soon found his man. "Here 'e is, your honor; an' a vile-looking heathen foreigner, too!"

"Steady now!" commanded Oglethorpe, as the weak frame of the Jew almost collapsed under the brutal force of the warden.

In the smoky flare of several torches the visitors saw an oval face, ghastly with the pallor of prison fever, and a mop of dark, untrimmed hair. Like spoke to like, however, and the visitors recognized a culture and intelligence in the delicate features of the Jew.

"Remove those chains!"

The warden tremblingly obeyed.

"Who are you, sir? Why are you here?" the General asked.

"I am Dr. Nunez, a physician of the Court of Portugal until one of my servants betrayed me, a Jew, to the Inquisition. With my wife and daughter, I fled to England. The remnants of my wealth I lost in 'the South Sea Bubble,' and a week ago my enemies, without warning, sent me here. Please notify my wife, for it is but a few shillings I need, and no message I sent seems ——"

The warden slyly kicked the prisoner's foot. "Don't listen to 'im, my lord; 'e's a bad 'un!"

Oglethorpe's piercing glance terrified the jailer. He fell on his knees. "My lord, I'll confess. The Lord High Chancellor fears this Jew's evidence, and ——"

"Enough!" said Oglethorpe, raising his hand. "Methinks the Earl himself will soon require the beggar's cage."

He opened his purse and took out a coin. "Here, friend Jew, take this, and be free."

Dr. Nunez declined with a courtly bow of simple dignity.

"Seignior," he pleaded, "not alms, but a friend!"

Oglethorpe held out his hand impulsively. "Friend, I am honored," he said. Then, indicating the youngest of his party, he continued, "My secretary, Charles Wesley, will note your good lady's address and you will be free before sun-down."

"There are others," pleaded Dr. Nunez, "who need your interest. Many of them are honest, hard-working men who, through sickness or misfortune, have contracted some trifling debt. Crushed by their burden of debts, fees and fines, the misery, shame and lack of food, they are in despair. If they offend their keepers they are subject to horrible punishments. Many have the symptoms of a hectic fever. I have ministered to them, but daily the angel of death visits us."

"I will pay the accounts of the worthy and release them," said Oglethorpe, deeply moved. "Then, in a new land, a colony shall be founded for them and for all who are unfortunate."

So powerful was the influence of General Oglethorpe that Thomas Bainbridge and the Lord High Chancellor of England were sentenced to Newgate prison at the same time that the first shipload of freed debtors left Gravesend, at the mouth of the River Thames, for the new colony in Georgia, where General James Edward Oglethorpe, its founder, had been appointed Governor of the colony.

As Charles Wesley and his brother, John, in obedience to the request of Oglethorpe, reached the home of Dr. Nunez, they were met at the door by a young man, who introduced himself as Abraham De Lyon.

"The doctor! The doctor! Any news of him?" he beseeched. "His family is distracted, and for nearly a week I have ceaselessly sought for him."

"He is safe," replied John Wesley, "and even now may be on his way home."

"God be praised! Isabel, your father is safe!" he cried, as a young girl threw open the door. "Is your mother better?" he tenderly asked.

"She is still prostrated; but—" the girl looked inquiringly at the two men.

Dr. Nunez arrived as the elder Wesley was explaining matters. Then the brothers departed. Abraham De Lyon was in a state of collapse now that the suspense was over.

"Remember," said Charles Wesley, in parting, "we are your friends—always."

Dr. Nunez' eyes filled with tears; Isabel impetuously kissed the hand of Charles Wesley; Abraham De Lyon was suffering from exhaustion.

So it came to pass that the little Jewish colony of London, after centuries of exile, seeking now its place in the great new empire that was to be, gathered its persecuted, poor and homeless members and chartered a vessel. Twenty Jewish families sailed a month later to help Governor Oglethorpe create the thirteenth colony in America.

On the 11th of July, Cockspur Island, smothered in Cherokee roses, was passed. Proceeding up the river, the ship anchored off a high bluff, from which Oglethorpe's white tent, a few huts, some cabins and a small fort, rimmed by dense vegetation, could be seen. This was the new settlement of Savannah.

Under a beautiful grove of mulberry trees the Governor was giving a public dinner to the colonists, who were assembled to receive their allotments of land and to organize a local government.

Dr. Nunez, leading the little company of two score Jews, approached the gaily decorated tables. The Wesley brothers, who were conversing with the Indian chief, Tomochichi, smiled a greeting, and the Governor welcomed them.

Trouble, however, was in store for the newcomers. Oglethorpe, in his desire to help the unfortunate, had overlooked grave faults in those he had assisted. The lazy demanded slaves; the dissolute, rum; and the discontented, the right to make their own laws. Mutiny was rampant, showing itself in the scowling faces of the discontented settlers.

"What have we here?" shouted William Bull, the land surveyor, pushing his way through the muttering crowd. "Jews and Catholics!"

"Catholics?" echoed Oglethorpe, puzzled.

"Look at those baubles on the women," the surveyor pointed out, the veins standing out on his neck with rage.

"Force of habit," Dr. Nunez gently replied. "These ladies, brought up in a Catholic country, cannot repeat their Hebrew prayers without the use of the rosary."

"Send them back, Governor. We don't want any Jews here," interrupted another.

"They will prejudice the success of the colony," muttered an old woman, shaking her head.

"What service can they render?" inquired William Stephens, cautiously.

"I hold the highest degree in medicine," replied Dr. Nunez.

"The Trustees desire that the settlers shall grow wine grapes, hemp, silk, the mulberry, and those medicinal plants which cannot be obtained from Spain because of the war. I am a horticulturist of Lisbon," answered Abraham De Lyon.

"We come not as pensioners on the King's bounty," said a white-haired elder. "We paid our own passage and come willing to work and to share your trials and triumphs. We have brought a scroll of the law and our religious objects, seeking only the same liberty in practicing our religion that we would grant you."

"Religion!" thundered William Bull. "We have too much religion already; what with the new-fangled religious methods of these Wesley brothers and their Holy Club meetings. They had better start a new religion, and call it Methodism. Ha, ha!!" He ended his tirade on a note of mockery.

Further discussion was postponed by the appearance of a caravel around the bend of the river.

Alarm seized the settlement, for the strange-looking little vessel was thought to be one of Blackbeard's pirate ships. Oglethorpe already suspected that some of his ex-convicts were in touch with the "Brethren of the Coast." The appearance of the Spanish flag, however, and the launching of a small boat under a flag of truce, lessened the suspense.

The smart young bugler who preceded the richly uniformed officer, blew a noisy summons, and announced, with the sweeping bow of old Spain, that Don Jose Morino y Redondo, Spanish Commissioner from Florida, claimed Georgia for his sovereign, and demanded their immediate evacuation.

The Governor bluntly ordered the Spaniards back to their ship, and thereupon, seeing that the colonists were making preparations for defense, the caravel hoisted sail and departed.

Immediately all thoughts of mutiny in the settlement disappeared, and, while the newcomers were disliked, their accounts of Spanish life were listened to with much interest.

Governor Oglethorpe organized his forces and directed the military defense. All was bustle and excitement.

Every man among the newcomers volunteered for military service and Jacob de la Motta, because of his experience in the Spanish army, was appointed captain over them.

Isabel helped her father gather and store medical herbs while all the women assisted in every way possible to prepare the colony for the coming storm. Thoughts of the savage and cruel Spanish soldiery gave courage, strength and unity to the little colony.

Then sudden reinforcements appeared. Ships arrived with great numbers of Protestant refugees from continental Europe who were seeking religious liberty. With the Lutherans from the Catholic city of Salzburg were a company of Jews under the leadership of Benjamin Sheftall. For the moment, the most useful addition to the settlement, however, was a regiment of six hundred Scotch Highlanders.

It was well that they arrived, for a Spanish army of three thousand were on their way to wipe out the audacious colonists.

The crafty Spaniards, however, had not relied entirely on force. Realizing that Oglethorpe, England's great general and organizer, was the source of power in the new colony, they had planned to remove him; and William Bull, who, as land surveyor, had once been in their employ, was their agent.

To him was given the task of stirring up discontent and mutiny among the settlers, alienating the Indians, and betraying the colony.

The coming of the Jews and other reinforcements had upset his plans. There remained but one way out—assassination and flight.

The Governor, leaving the settlement in charge of Macdonald, the Scotch colonel, had gone through the surrounding forests with William Bull, Dr. Nunez and Abraham De Lyon on an exploring trip, when a shot rang out. Oglethorpe staggered and sat down on a fallen oak. Clapping a hand to his shoulder, he cried, as he saw the fleeing surveyor through the trees, "You traitor!" Then, growing weak, he muttered, "Can this be the end?"

Dr. Nunez hastened to his relief, while Tomochichi, the Indian, brought the traitor down with an arrow.

Skilful fingers removed the bullet. Abraham De Lyon found some wild thyme.

"What is that?" asked Oglethorpe, as the sweet-smelling poultice was cleverly bandaged.

"We Jews call it hyssop," remarked the doctor with a smile. "It will staunch the flow of blood, cleanse, and soothe the wound."

Savannah was in an uproar, and it needed all the eloquence of the Wesleys to pacify the wrath of the people against the plotters.

Then the Highlanders marched off to meet the Spaniards, while the Governor, in the shade of his tent, wrote the Trustees a full and clear account of the eventful happenings of the day, praising the Jews for their enterprise and worth, and calling special attention to those who had been of such great assistance in the day of trouble.

"DUTCH, Swedes, Germans, Lutherans, Negroes, Protestants, Quakers, Catholics, and Jews. In no other colony are there so many different races and religions represented. Surely 'tis God's will that we, His Clansmen, should see to it that this colony be kept racially pure and single in religion?"

The speaker, a stout and florid Englishman, paused for breath, while his audience of two score men filling a sumptuous chamber in Clarke Hall, Philadelphia, one evening in the year 1740, shouted their approval of the speaker's sentiments.

At the head of a long mahogany table, doubled up in wine-sodden drunkenness, his face hidden behind the black mask which the Clansmen of that day wore, presided Will Penn, the young and dissolute son of the greater founder of the colony.

Weak-willed and constantly flattered, he was easily

127

led by crafty men whose ambition was to maintain by terror the control of the colony's government, which was now slipping from the hands of visionary Quakers into those of sterner and more practical pioneers of hardier stock.

"And the Indians also," exclaimed a young man springing to his feet, "they, too, have been over-much pampered and petted. 'Tis time we changed the weak and cowardly policy of ——"

Judge Quarry, the first speaker and real leader of the Clansmen, raised a warning hand and quickly glanced at the boyish figure at the head of the table.

The youth, John Evans, subsided.

Poor Will Penn! The schemers used his honored name, while in contempt they tolerated him as "chief." Many a beaver-hatted, drab-cloaked Quaker shook his head in sadness at the son's dissipation, which had brought the great father of the colony to an untimely end.

Then spoke David Clark. "I bring you news from Lancaster village," he said, "where I act as wagon-man for Colonel Lowrey and old Simon, his Jewish partner. 'Tis of them I speak and of the tragic event that is about to happen to this fair land of ours unless we, the Clansmen of God, prevent it."

"Aye, we will!" roared a dozen eager voices in reply.

"Know ye then," David Clark continued, his eyes gleaming with anger through the black mask, "that there is a plot to create a new colony to be named Western Virginia, from the vast lands which the Jews of Lancaster have by treaty secured from the Indians."

"The Clan should prevent this," remarked Judge Quarry, turning to Will Penn.

The hall clock struck the midnight hour.

"The Clan rides!" the young chief cried, closing the great gilt-edged Bible open before him, and stumbling to his feet.

This action denoted the close of the session.

"Get weapons and torches! To horse! Then to Lancaster! Before the sun sets again we will write the will of God in bloody, fiery letters, if need be." It was the voice of Jonas Claypoole, the most active and fierce Clansman of them all.

With a noisy cheer, the company dispersed.

Then into the darkness of a moonless night rode more than a score of horsemen. The smoky glare of torches on masked faces and the sound of hoofs rattling over cobblestones brought terror to many a peaceful citizen. The riders swept past cherry orchards and quiet farms and took the direct road to the village of Lancaster, some sixty miles west.

Fording or leaping the streams, picking their way through pine forests, where the wolves, like themselves, still hunted in packs, they rode through the valleys and over the hills. Hour by hour, silent and stern, they continued until they reached the hut of

Michael Weaders, a skin-dresser, who lived within half a mile of their destination.

Here they decided to halt and seek information.

Receiving no immediate reply to his call, Claypoole finally backed his horse against the rickety door and, without effort, broke it down.

A half-witted old man appeared. "Good masters," he quavered, "what is wrong? I—" Then, at the sight of the feared, hated Clansmen, he uttered a feeble cry and fainted.

Stepping over his prostrate body, Jonas Claypoole strode into the hovel, to receive with rough force over his head and shoulders and in his face, a home-made birch-broom wielded by an angry, white-haired, little old woman.

The stiff twigs tore off his mask as he put his hands up to protect his face.

"Ah, 'tis you, Jonas Claypoole!" she screamed. "Fine upholder of law and order, great lawyer, though ye be! Take that! You and your cowardly crew of rowdies riding through the country, scaring old folks out of their wits. Get thee gone!"

As her voice rose to a scream, the lowered broom caught between Claypoole's legs, causing the leading lawyer and wealthiest man in Philadelphia to trip backwards and roll over, and out through the door into the newly-manured and muddy vegetable patch.

The laughter of his comrades aroused him to fury.

He roared and cursed, "I'll throw her into yon

Claypoole tripped and rolled over.

whortleberry swamp, the old witch." Twisting his hand in the collar of her dress he dragged the screaming woman to the rough plank bridge over the deepest part of the swamp, and with a contemptuous kick pushed her in. Then, without a glance at the bubbling spot of his crime, he strode back to the little group of solemn-faced Clansmen.

Beneath the black masks the light of reason was dimly struggling for expression in the minds of several. Young Penn began to weep in maudlin protest, while even Judge Quarry remarked that it was hardly necessary for them to drown old women in order to preserve the colony from the alien.

Sullenly and silently, the smarting Claypoole began to ride on, followed by the whole troop. Before long a volley of iron nails, bolts and scrap-iron from the ancient blunderbuss of old Weaders, hidden in the woods, caused much annoyance to the brave Clansmen. One of them even fainted from the loss of blood occasioned by a broken nose, caused by a three-inch iron bolt from the old man's vicious gun.

It was an angry company of men who rode that morning into Penn Square, the center of the little village of Lancaster.

The few inhabitants who were about speedily disappeared.

The Clansmen rode around the green, reverently peered into the little Episcopal Church, passed the Quaker meeting-house without stopping, and after raiding the village inn, continued down the street to the closed and barred store which David Clark had pointed out as that of the Indian traders, Alexander Lowrey and Joseph Simon.

"That Scotchman and Jew have been in partnership for over forty years," Clark told them. "Having now reached the allotted term of three score years and ten, they have settled their accounts peacefully, in spite of the fact that nothing was written in black and white; and now young Levy and Gratz are to continue it while these older men, with other Jews, are to develop the West Virginian colony of which I spoke."

"And thus deprive us English gentlemen of our right to govern," added Judge Quarry, with an oath.

"Break down the doors," thundered Claypoole, still anxious for revenge, "and we'll show them who rules in this country." He viciously kicked at the door.

"Look out for guns!" Judge Quarry warned. "The Jews are as crafty as Indians."

"And look out for brooms, hic!" came the mocking voice of Will Penn, reeling against the village pump, on which still burned the lamp whose solitary light lit the village at night.

The lamp caught his notice; he gave a drunken laugh and flung it at the door of the storehouse. "Burn 'em out, hic!" he ordered.

Before the Clansmen could obey, however, a fresh diversion caught their attention.

Nearby stood the pillory, stocks, and whipping post, in front of the prison cage.

"There are Indians in here," said a Clansman, peering through the prison bars.

It was like a spark to gunpowder.

Claypoole's eyes lit up with joy. Here was a chance for vengeance, for who would protect the savages?

"Break open the door, Clansmen!" he cried. "We will make such an example of them that it will be a warning to all their cursed race."

Quickly they broke the door in and the alarmed Indians were dragged out.

Their leader began to explain how firewater had been given them, causing them to riot and thus be imprisoned.

The impatient Claypoole, waiting no longer, struck the Indian down with the heavy butt of his great horse pistol.

Another Indian, suddenly drawing a hidden hunting knife, buried it in the Clansman's chest, and the latter fell lifeless across the prostrate body of his Indian victim.

Then things happened quickly. Within a few minutes six helpless red men had been massacred by the infuriated white men.

"Now for the Jews, Clansmen!" shouted John Evans.

The trading place of Lowrey and Simon was the largest store in Lancaster. Solidly built of massive logs by Swedish pioneers as a trading-post and fort in the early days, the many additions, barns and stables, made it a settlement within itself.

"Force open that door, Clansmen!" cried Judge Quarry. "We will deal calmly with them about the matter we came upon. I like not this senseless killing of old women and defenseless Indians."

Before hands could be laid on the door, however, it was suddenly opened and a little, rotund, dark-complexioned Jew appeared.

"Welcome, Clansmen, welcome!" he suavely said, apparently unafraid of his visitors.

Several Clansmen pushed rudely into the great hall-like room. A little group of men stood by an immense fireplace at one end of the cabin.

"Jews and gentiles," remarked Judge Quarry sourly as he glanced over them. "You that are not Jews come over here by the door," he ordered roughly.

Several stepped out from the group in obedience to his command.

Seizing one of them by the shoulder, Judge Quarry said, evidently puzzled as well as annoyed, "How is it that you so demean your race and nation, for I perceive that you are of British stock, by associating with these alien intruders?" He glanced contemptuously over the little group of Jews.

"I am but a servant, master," the young man boldly replied. "I have no dealings with them except that of wages. Their money is good, and Colonel Alexander Lowrey himself ——"

"Ah, where is he?" broke in the Clansman quickly. "Let him stand forth."

The Jew who had opened the door stepped forward. "He is not here, Judge Quarry," he said quietly.

"How come you to know my name?" the startled Clansman demanded angrily. "And who are you?"

The Jew bowed low to hide the twinkle in his eyes. "I am Joseph Simon, part owner here. The names of all the Clansmen are known to us. Your masks deceive none but Clansmen. Why not remove them, gentlemen?"

"I've a good mind to run you through with my sword," a young Clansman snapped, stepping toward him, threateningly.

"Dishonor not your father's worthy weapon, John Evans," Joseph Simon replied gently.

"Heaven on earth!" shouted Judge Quarry. "How come you to know our names, I say?"

"Ask our wagon-man who is among you; perhaps he ——"

The Clansmen angrily turned upon one of their number standing in the doorway.

"The Jew lies," shouted David Clark. Impulsively he raised his pistol and fired at his accuser, whose quick eye had detected him.

The bullet buried itself in a ceiling beam. Judge Quarry had struck up Clark's arm as he fired. "No more wanton bloodshed," he said sternly, "or the country will arise against us."

Then, turning to Simon, he said, "Jew, we have come about a certain transaction of yours that we forbid. Our forefathers erected in this land the standard of England and the Established Church. They, with children of their breed, shall forever rule this colony. This treaty between Jew and savage pertaining to vast lands beyond the mountains to be developed as a new colony must not be consummated.

"We wish you no harm," he continued more kindly, "but you—of an alien race and religion should never have been permitted to enter this sylvan land."

"And the Swedes and the Dutch before you?" questioned Simon with a smile. "Do they not consider you aliens, even as you consider us?"

"We are of true English stock," replied Judge Quarry proudly. "There stands William Penn, the son of England's famous admiral and personal friend of our sovereign lord, the King, and we, like him, are all sons of Christian English gentlemen, the salt of the earth." He glanced haughtily at the silent group of Jews and his lips curled in disdain.

"Then listen, Christian gentlemen," said the Jew softly, but with such earnestness that all paid heed to his words: "You want this treaty for the Western lands, legal though it be, annulled. Then let the government of this colony rule upon it. Is that not just? Is that not English?

"'The Clan Rides!' is your call. Men's faces pale, women shriek, and children cry when they hear it. Is that Christian?

"Do you see yon barred doors? Behind them are our women; we Jews are fully armed and will give our lives to protect those bars from being removed. Do you blame us?"

"The Jew speaks fair," remarked Judge Quarry, turning to Will Penn at his side.

"Moreover," continued Joseph Simon, his dark face flushed with determination, "in the cellar under our feet our stock of gunpowder is piled high, the train is laid, and young Levy sits on a barrel ready to blow us all into eternity at one sign from me. Terror will be met with terror, though we all perish!"

The Clansmen instinctively backed toward the door, where a sudden commotion arose as a powerfully built, rugged Scotchman, his sandy hair plentifully streaked with white, elbowed his way in with his musket across his shoulder.

He glanced around in astonishment; then, seizing Judge Quarry by the shoulder, he roared, "Dinna ye ken, mon, ye're trespassing! Oot wi' ye!"

The Clansman brushed aside the restraining hand; then, looking into the face of the angry Scotchman, he started and gasped in amazement. Tearing off his mask, he placed a hand on each shoulder of the newcomer and said, "Are you Alexander Lowrey of Glengarry, chief of the Clan Macdonald?"

The dour Scotchman nodded.

"I thought so," the Clansman said, "the plague marks in your face remind me of that terrible three-months' sea voyage at our first coming from England." Then, turning to the young Penn at his side, he continued, "When smallpox visited our becalmed, famine-cursed ship, this heroic Scotchman, risking an awful death, nursed many of us back to health and life and saved for America your father, William Penn. To the courage of Lowrey, I owe my life."

The Scotchman's only reply was to point his gun at the group of Clansmen. "Oot yon door-r-r!" he commanded, "ye muckle-headed fools; oot!"

Without a word the Clansmen silently filed out into the open air.

"I want ye to understond," he continued as he stood facing them at the open door, "ye are as unweelcome here as I was in yon city of brotherly love, where the gentry, the 'quality,' as ye call them, made mock of my marked face, my empty purse and left me to starve.

"So I made fre-ends wi' your unwanted Jew and despised savage, and found them honest.

"'Twas here that our William Penn himself deeded us these lands, and no mon's wor-r-d, Jew, gentile or Indian, has need to be written, for here mon deals fair wi' mon, and ne'er a dispute until your ungodly Clan came to disturb our peace. Will Penn, thou chief of this evil Clan, begone!"

While he was speaking, an old wizened man, chattering to himself, had ambled almost unnoticed up to the door. In his blue eyes was a look of insanity.

Suddenly throwing open his long cloak, Michael Weaders revealed a blunderbuss. He pointed its broad, bell-like mouth at Will Penn, and echoing Lowrey's words, "Will Penn, thou chief of this evil Clan, begone!" he fired.

Judge Quarry by a fraction of a second had thrown himself in front of his young friend and received the motley contents of the weapon in his chest.

With a low moan he sank to the ground.

Lowrey tenderly raised the wounded man. Simon and two Clansmen gently laid him on a pile of soft furs inside the store.

At the call of Simon, John Evans quickly threw down the bars of one of the side rooms and a young Jewess hastened out.

"Quick, Miriam, water, linens, and salves," cried Simon, her father.

Little could be done, however, for the wounded man; his life was rapidly ebbing away.

"Forgive me," he presently murmured as he looked into the sympathetic faces of those around him. "I have been wrong. My pride did ruin me; I knew not what I did."

Then through the mists that were fast gathering in his eyes, he saw the soft, effeminate face of his young chief, whose life he had just saved. Reaching out, he placed Penn's soft hand in the huge, rugged palm of Lowrey's and whispered, "Nurse him, even as you nursed his father."

Then came delirium. As fading memories turned back the pages of time, he suddenly raised himself on one arm and cried, "The Clan rides!"

"—no more," added Will Penn, as he sadly laid his friend back on the furs.

A touch of his great father's determined resolution and manliness had come at last to Will Penn, and he spoke gently to Simon, and smiled at Miriam. Then he fell, shedding bitter tears of repentance, on Lowrey's friendly shoulder.

Deeply impressed, the Clansmen removed their masks, and one by one, quietly and solemnly slipped out of the open door into the sunshine.

I, MICHAEL FRANKS, a mere Jewish peddler of gim-cracks and gewgaws among the Indians, sat in the window-seat of the Blue Anchor Inn watching the scene before me.

It was an April morning in 1755. The little village of Alexandria, situated on the west bank of the Potomac, not far from the sea, was gay with flags and bunting. King Street, its usually quiet, shady, main highway, resounded to the cheerful chatter of visiting "tide-water aristocracy," as the stern, rough frontiers-men contemptuously termed the well-established coast-line communities.

The cause of all this happy expectancy was due to the presence in the village of the Governors of Massa-chusetts, Pennsylvania, Maryland, and New York, who, with Governor Morris of Virginia, had met to confer with the English general, Edward Braddock, regarding the safety of the colonies and the protection of the western settlements.

A special service had been held in Christ Church this morning, and now all the great people of state and society who had sought the blessing of Divine Providence in the war that had been decided upon against the French and their Indian allies were pouring out of the little edifice.

Two regiments of the King's famous Coldstream Grenadier Guards, recently arrived from England, stood in statuesque, silent attention, drawn up in long ranks facing the church door. Their colors fluttered proudly in the breeze and the brilliant spring sun flashed from their polished accoutrements. Our young people clustered around in wide-eyed wonderment at such martial glory so freely displayed to such poor homespun and gingham as we represented.

The colonials, having left the church first, stood outside the doors, an interested and expectant crowd; the five Governors, with their families, appeared from within the church, followed by navy and Royal Artillery officers in blue and gold. Then, as the military band played "God Save the King," General Edward Braddock, his chest covered with medals won on the continent of Europe, strutted out, his sabre clanking against the stone steps of the little church.

He had eyes for none save his beloved guards.

"Attent'n! Right tur-r-rn!! For-war-r-r-d march!!!" barked their colonel.

Gallantly the British troops swept past, smooth as water down a mill-race. The music had stopped, but the steady rhythmical drum-beats and the soul-stirring step of twelve hundred men in unison, thrilled all hearts.

The colors dipped and the officers raised their flashing swords in salute as they passed their general, standing proudly on the holystoned and whitened steps of the church. He glanced superciliously over Colonel George Washington's motley company—Daniel Boone and his fellow-adventurers in buckskin and fur; the young artillerymen from Massachusetts; the Washington family, and Benjamin Franklin, with whom General Braddock had quarreled that morning. Franklin had dared to suggest that every redcoat might be "a living target to an unseen foe" as soon as they entered the primeval forests.

Across the village green our colonial militia was drawn up in silent, blue-coated companies.

To my surprise, I recognized among them, in Captain Mercer's company, Jacob Myer. We, two lonely Jews, had come from England together in the same ship; he to work for a term of years on the Faucett brothers' tobacco plantation in return for the passage money advanced to him, and I to barter and trade with the Indians. We had become firm friends, although my many journeys into the great western wilderness had prevented us from meeting often.

At the first opportunity, I crossed the green and

called to him. He seized my two hands, his dark eyes sparkling with pleasure. "Oh, Michael, how I have missed you," he cried.

"What are you doing here, Jacob?" I asked in amazement. "I thought you were miles away, on the Faucett plantation."

His face clouded. "To blazes with them!" he growled. "They stole my indenture papers and then claimed that I had signed for seven years' service to them instead of five. We quarreled, and I struck Joseph Faucett down with a strip of wood from a broken tobacco-drying rack. I fled the Virginia militia."

"You didn't kill—" I began, seizing his arm in alarm lest his violent action might fan into flames the spirit of hatred and intolerance toward our people that, alas, lies so near the surface in many men.

As though in answer to my inquiry, a body of men came riding into the little village at full gallop, and I recognized among their leaders Thomas and Joseph Faucett.

"The savages are on the warpath!" they cried, "and are destroying and massacring on every side." Then, the newcomers began to pour out vivid stories of Indian horrors and of the terror-stricken men, women, and children who were fleeing to Alexandria in every kind of vehicle and on foot.

"The savages fired our settlements and destroyed our growing tobacco," continued Tom Faucett, addressing himself to Colonel George Washington, who had been left in charge now that the last battery of General Braddock's Royal Artillery had rumbled out of sight toward Mr. Harper's ferry, where they were to cross the river in their expedition against the French. "We barely escaped with our lives," he concluded.

"So I see," replied Colonel Washington, nodding toward Joseph Faucett whose head was wrapped in blood-stained bandages.

"No Indian did that," growled Joseph Faucett, "but our runaway bond-servant, Jacob Myer. Why, there he is over there! Seize him! There's another Jew, too! The country's full of them, and they won't work; they're too independent! Down with the cursed race; away with the Jews!"

His friends took up the cry of hate, vengeance, and intolerance.

Colonel Washington stilled the angry crowd with a word. "This is no time for personal quarrels," he said calmly. "Our militia and the volunteers' company need recruits. Who will join? We follow General Braddock."

Shouting their compliance, the brothers with their friends galloped off to join the colonial volunteers. Since Jacob needed what little protection I could give at this critical time, I gripped my musket which had provided many a meal of wild duck and pigeon and protection from roving mountain lions while on my various western trips. Making a sudden decision, I joined Captain Van Braam's company of militia.

Under Colonel Washington's orderly command all our arrangements were rapidly completed. Guided by experienced backwoodsmen, who acted as scouts, we took the road which General Braddock had considered too rough, and within a few days overtook the slow-moving British general who stopped to level every mole-hill and bridge every brook so that the ranks of his soldiers might not be disturbed in their marching.

General Braddock was in an ill-humor and cursed everything American, but it was plain to see that Colonel Washington had risen in his estimation.

The month of May passed and June found us struggling through the woods, buried in the dense greenery of early summer.

Thus we reached the Youghiogheny River, fifteen miles from our destination, Fort Duquesne, which the general had planned to seize and rename Pitts-Bourgh in honor of a great English statesman.

Early on the morning of the 9th of July, the little army, having crossed the river, was marching in perfect order along its northern bank. I heard Colonel Washington remark that the display of the British troops on this eventful sunrise was the most beautiful spectacle he had ever beheld.

Every man was neatly dressed in full uniform; the soldiers were arranged in columns and marched in exact order; the sun gleamed from their burnished arms; the river flowed tranquilly on their right, and on the left the deep forest overshadowed them with solemn grandeur.

Suddenly from out of the silent woods a heavy discharge of musketry swept the ranks of our advance-guard of royal troops. But no enemy was to be seen.

The general hastened forward to the relief of the advanced parties; but, before he could reach the spot which they occupied, they gave way and fell back upon the artillery and the other columns of the army, causing extreme confusion, and striking the whole mass with such a panic that no order could afterwards be restored. The general and the officers behaved with the utmost courage, using every effort to rally the men and bring them to order, but all in vain. They huddled together in half-formed platoons and columns while the unseen French and Indians shot down the brilliantly conspicuous soldiers in dozens.

Again and again did Colonel Washington lead his companies into the woods for hand-to-hand fighting; but so well protected were our enemies that each little group was wiped out, the colonel himself barely escaping with his life.

Then the proud Coldstream Guards, their military organization shaken, their officers fallen, broke all restraint and ignominiously fled, leaving us, the despised militia and contemptible volunteers, to face the unseen, terrible foe.

Through the crowd of fleeing soldiers I saw Jacob Myer a few yards ahead of me, standing amid scattered bodies of dead and wounded men. He was firing wildly at puffs of smoke that betokened the enemy's presence. Then from among the prostrate figures a hand reached up, seized him by the ankle, and roughly pulled him down.

It was Daniel Boone, the pioneer adventurer. The wisdom of his rough counsel to Jacob to take cover was so obvious that I crawled through the tall grass to their side and protected myself somewhat behind the bodies of several guardsmen whose gorgeous uniforms had been their ruin. We kept up a continuous fire under Boone's direction.

Raging like the British lion that he so ably represented, and waving his sword in his left hand—his right arm helpless from a wound in his shoulder—General Braddock rode along in front of the little groups of colonials. His face was purple with rage and he almost stood in his stirrups.

"Out in the open, cowards!" he roared. "Fight like Englishmen! Form ranks and the enemy will flee!"

Thus voicing his experience, which had never failed on the battlefields of Flanders, the general bullied and thundered. But we colonials were angry; the glamor of royal militarism had forever vanished from our minds. We gritted our teeth, tightened our belts, clenched our weapons and looked to Washington, our colonel, the coolest, bravest fighter on that tragic battlefield, and resolved to serve him to the bitter end.

Thus baffled, General Braddock, in his anger, struck with the back of his sword at Joseph Faucett, who was at that moment seeking cover behind a friendly dogwood bush. The sword slipped, and poor Joseph fell to the ground with the weapon buried in his neck. A moment later, the general pitched headlong over the head of his horse, a bullet through his chest.

Colonel Washington was now the commanding officer, with barely a subaltern left to carry out orders.

A few moments later, amid the whistling bullets flying around him, for he was a marked man, he rode past us. "The Virginia Blues will retire in good order, carrying their wounded," he announced calmly, "and take advantage of every cover," he concluded.

A spontaneous cheer came from every throat. Our loyalty to him and to each other was from that moment sealed. We fell back, stubbornly fighting every inch of the way; the drab-colored little company of volunteers heroically guarding our rear.

General Braddock, carried off the field, first on a gun-carriage, then on horseback, and finally by four of his guardsmen, expired. By the light of the moon he was buried in the middle of the rough road, the troops passing over his grave to prevent its violation by the Indians.

Thus we reached a planter's settlement. Daniel Boone, returning from scout duty, reported that Pontiac's Indians could not be tempted from scenes of carnage and plunder, and that the French were too few to act without their guidance and aid. Colonel Washington then decided to halt for the balance of the night.

Thoroughly wearied by our terrible experience, our companies sought no better shelter that warm July night than the friendly cover of fresh green hedges.

From the depths of a sound sleep, however, I was roughly aroused by a hand shaking my shoulder. Awakening, I found Daniel Boone's hand over my mouth. Without a word, I followed him to where Jacob was standing. With a finger on his lips to denote silence, he led us to the planter's dwelling. A sign to the watchful sentry at the door, and we were allowed to enter. Tapping on the door of an inner room, it was opened to us, and we found ourselves in the presence of Colonel Washington, seated at a table. Tom Faucett was standing facing the colonel. We saluted and lined up alongside of Faucett, the four of us in a row opposite the colonel. He looked up at us across the table. Then, turning toward Tom Faucett, he said, "Now, tell your story again."

"I repeat, Colonel, I saw this Jew, Jacob Myer, shoot down General Braddock."

In my indignant surprise at such a statement I forgot the presence of the colonel, and turning toward Faucett, who was standing next to me, I struck him on the mouth.

"It's a vicious, preposterous lie!" I shouted indignantly. "He was killed by the enemy."

Colonel Washington raised a hand for silence. He then unrolled a strip of purple silk, which I recognized as General Braddock's sash, significantly stained in one spot a darker crimson. A flattened bullet rolled out.

The colonel pointed to the British Government's mark—a broad arrow—stamped on the end of it. "The surgeon probed this from the general's chest," he said quietly. "The question is, who fired it?"

"Thomas Faucett!" rasped Daniel Boone.

"You lie!" snapped Faucett sharply.

"Colonel," continued the scout, "my eyes see all! I saw Faucett raise his rifle and shoot Braddock down a moment after the general had struck down his brother Joseph."

The colonel nodded understandingly. A dead silence followed for several moments, then, seeing his defeat, Faucett changed his tactics and began to speak hurriedly, "Yes, Colonel, I fired that shot. General Braddock, curse him, murdered my brother. To avenge his death, to save myself, my comrades, you— yea, even the whole army from that . . . listen, what noise is that?"

From across the river nearby the shrieks of the Indians' prisoners came fitfully to our ears, blanching our faces as open warfare had never done.

Again the colonel nodded understandingly.

"With you in command," continued Faucett, "there was a chance for escape; but with that stubborn fool ——"

"Enough!" ordered the colonel sharply. "There is truth in what you say; but ——"

A long silence ensued disturbed only by the sentry's step and the horrible sounds in the distance.

"Foolish Braddock," murmured the colonel at last. Then, arousing himself, he said: "Now, Faucett, you fought bravely, and have suffered much; but it was a dastardly act to accuse this innocent Jew. Know this," and he spoke slowly, solemnly and with deep feeling, "there will come a time when there will be neither Jew nor gentile, rich nor poor, master nor servant—only American patriots." Another pause; then he continued: "But what shall I do with you? If I turn you over to Colonel Dunbar, my superior, when we reach camp, what will the English troops, and the British Government do to you, if they are told that this fatal bullet came from your rifle?"

"Colonel," Daniel Boone spoke, "those of us from the inland settlements are striking camp tonight in order to warn the border settlers of the failure of this expedition. We take our lives in our hands, and most of us may share the fate of those poor wretches over the river. Let Tom Faucett come with us; he is a brave man, at least, and ——"

Faucett seized Daniel Boone's hand and wrung it in gratitude. Then, after a moment's hesitation, he

153

shook Jacob's hand and mine. "Some day," he said, as he saluted the colonel, "we may all meet again, for there is more trouble brewing than we imagine. English methods and American ideas will not mix."

For the third time, Colonel Washington nodded understandingly, and there appeared in his inscrutable eyes a faraway look, as though he could see many things unknown to us of the common herd.

This, then, is the story of the most tragic and disastrous of any expedition ever sent out. Though we all went through the shadows, the hand of God was over us. The genius of our Washington was shown through his superior's failure. The emptiness of mere pomp and display was revealed, and we two Jews, tried in the fiery furnace, even as our ancestors of old, came out of our trials better able to stand the dangers and the tribulations of the great Revolution that shortly came upon us. Finally, under the guidance of Daniel Boone, a loyal American and true friend, we found the gateway of the West opened to us, and we passed in safety to the land flowing with milk and honey—the first of many thousands that followed.

IT WAS "Guy Fawkes' Day" in London, in the year
1755, and everywhere the young people were shoot-
ing firecrackers and burning straw-stuffed "guys" to
celebrate the one hundred and fiftieth anniversary
of the discovery of the "Gunpowder Plot" to destroy
both King and Parliament.

I drew my cloak around me, for the yellow blanket
of fog seemed horribly damp, because I had just returned from sunny Portugal. I hurried through the
district of "Old Jewry" to my destination, the beautiful house in White Hart Court, by the Bishop's Gate,
where the brothers Joseph and Francis Salvador,
financial agents for the British Government, trans-
acted business of importance.

My sharp rat-tat of the brass door-knocker brought
me speedy entrance, and I found the brothers alone
in their office-home, bright with many candles and

warmed by a cozy log fire in the open fireplace.

"Welcome home, Moses Lindo," cried Francis, the younger brother, impulsively kissing me on the cheek as was our Portuguese custom. Joseph, from his deep-seated chair, smiled and raised his hand in greeting.

I noticed with sorrow that the old man had grown weaker during the months I had been away.

Learning that I had not eaten, my friends insisted that I should partake of a meal before entering into business details; Francis meanwhile was keeping up a rather one-sided conversation.

"Our efforts with the Colonial Office," he said, "have resulted in our purchase of one hundred thousand acres near Charles Town in the Province of South Carolina, for settlement by our people."

" 'Tis good news," I replied, "and my proposition for the cultivation of the indigo plant there?"

He laughed with an embarrassed air. "Your pet scheme finds no backers. It has been tried before, it seems, and——"

"The planters did not use wisdom," I remarked. "Many a rare herb used in chemistry and medicine grows wild in that ideal climate and soil."

Still unconvinced, Francis shook his head. Then, after a few moments' silence, he asked, "Was your journey a success, Moses?"

"It was," I replied. "King Joseph of Portugal will accept the loan of his ally, the King of England, made through us."

"But our people?" Deeply moved, Joseph Salvador had risen to his feet, a white-haired patriarch protecting his people. "Will Joseph of Portugal deal justly with our people if this loan be floated?"

"He will," I replied slowly. "But the God of our fathers moves in a mysterious way ——"

Francis suddenly placed his hands on my shoulders. Looking straight into my eyes, he said: "What is wrong, Moses? You are not your usual calm self."

As though in answer to his inquiry the door was thrown open and David Cohen, the bookkeeper, rushed in.

"The earthquake!" he cried. "Portugal has been rocked by earthquakes. In the twinkling of an eye, Lisbon is become a heap of ruins, burying its people, while tidal waves and fires have swept away our investments. Shipping quays, warehouses, and property, all are gone! We are ruined! Woe to Israel!"

"Alas, 'tis only too true!" I remarked. "I fled through Spain and France on the swiftest horses to reach and warn you, but—look at Joseph!"

The old man's head had sunk upon his breast, and his long white beard lay mirrored in the polished mahogany table before him. We gently raised him, but a spasm of the heart had laid hold of him and his spirit had fled. The shock had been too great. Death had dissolved the firm; the great Dutch East India Company had lost its pilot, England her financial agent, our London congregation its leader, and, save for my small allotment in the sandy soil of the "Jews' land" of South Carolina, I faced the world penniless.

Leaving the house of sudden mourning, I decided to visit my friend, the secretary of the Royal Society, Emanuel da Costa, with whom I had spent much time in chemical research, and, remembering that he would be at the Gresham College where William Herschel, one of the brightest of our younger men, was lecturing on astronomy, I called a passing sedan-chair and bade the two chairmen carry me toward the center of the city.

So dense was the fog, however, that my carriers soon lost their way, and in rounding a corner in their hurry, they collided with a similar "chair" coming from the opposite direction.

A volley of curses, the sound of breaking glass and a girl's scream followed.

It was the sedan-chair of a lady of quality. Her men wore the livery of a titled person, the smoky flare of a passing link-boy's torch showing the gold-edged capes of their purple overcoats.

The men's faces were pale with terror as they lifted the young girl from the wreckage. They stepped back as I, bowing, murmured apologies and offered my sedan-chair with my services and protection if she so desired.

With an engaging smile of innocence on an unblemished face free from rouge and cosmetics so usual

The terrified men stepped back.

in court life, a somewhat affrighted voice answered: " 'Tis nothing; I am not hurt. This fog is so blinding that we have lost our way home from my birthday party. Please give me your arm."

I led her to my chair and ordered my men to carry her, while her footmen, preceded by the torch-boy, walked ahead a few paces and inquired the way.

Thus we reached the large brown-stone mansion of the Earl of Bute, in the aristocratic section of May-fair.

"May I leave you now?" I asked.

"Nay, sir," she replied. "I have brought you so far from your own business that I pray you to accept a little refreshment before you go on your way. The Earl would take it amiss if I let you leave so churl-ishly."

Therefore I entered the mansion, where the Earl of Bute, a red-faced, loud-voiced member of the aristocracy, gave me a boisterous welcome.

"There'll be the devil to pay when Sir Charles hears of this, by gad," he roared. "The poor fool is so insanely jealous he will turn green with envy at your good fortune in bringing the Princess home."

"Princess!" I echoed, amazed.

"Yes, a Princess of one of the German states, Mecklenburg, to be exact."

"Oh! I have lost my ring!" the girl exclaimed. "The ring sent from my home across the seas for my birth-day today."

"Then, your Highness, its jewel should be a topaz," I replied with a smile, "for the yellow topaz is the November stone, bringing you a message of friendship and success."

"Correct, friend, correct!" she exclaimed, her eyes sparkling with glee. "How strange that a big serious man like you should know the sentiment of jewels!"

"Ah, your Highness, who should know it better than those of our race who for generations have had to conceal their wealth in jewels?"

Then, as she appeared interested, I told her of the earthquake, of the Salvador brothers, our proposed settlement in America, and my own ambitions in the matter of the indigo trade there.

"Are you going to the Carolina plantations?" she queried.

"I had no intention of going there," I said, "but perhaps ——"

"Do so," she interrupted impulsively. "There you will find success, I am sure."

When, after refreshments had been served, a servant brought my hat, gloves and greatcoat, a small gold ring with a yellow topaz set in it fell from the folded cuff of my overcoat.

I picked it up and handed it to the young girl, saying, "It must have fallen as you entered my sedan-chair."

With a bright smile she held it out to me. "It has returned to me at an opportune moment," she said.

"Will you accept it as a token of my friendship and desire for your success?"

"Your Highness," I replied after a moment's hesitation, "I will, with the greatest of pleasure."

*　　*　　*

Before the month ended I sailed for America, and after a stormy voyage the ship anchored off the city of Charles Town, in the province of South Carolina.

Many members of the newly organized Beth Elohim congregation together with Rabbi Isaac da Costa came down to Half Moon Wharf to welcome me, and I found the three thousand inhabitants of the delightful little town well disposed toward our people.

The inviting fresh green of its Broad Way stretching for several miles through the settlements, invited me, and as soon as I could I hurried off to view that last purchase of Joseph Salvador, the "Jews' land."

From the highest twig of a roadside bush a sprightly little warbler in a coat of purplish-blue with ever-changing tints welcomed me with its canary-like song. I recognized it as the famous indigo bird.

It was a happy omen. I felt that it meant success.

But, try as I might, I could not interest my fellow Jews in the growing of indigo.

Disheartened, I stood by the river's bank one morning, soon after my arrival, moodily watching a boat being rowed from a newly arrived frigate-of-war.

A young man in the smart uniform of an English

Vice-Admiral leapt briskly out of the boat, and, to my astonishment, I heard him mention my name.

I stepped up to him inquiringly and announced myself.

He glanced over me superciliously and his face flushed crimson with rage as he saw on my finger the topaz ring of the Princess.

"Sirrah," he said, "I have come all the way from England to ask you a question."

I bowed and waited for him to continue.

"Do you value that ring very highly?" he asked.

"For sentimental reasons, I do," I replied, nettled at his impertinence.

"Dammit!" he muttered, "I knew it!" Then I saw mad, unreasoning jealousy raging in his eyes.

"But the Princess is naught to me," I added.

His face lit up with a smile of relief. "But you wear the ring she gave you?" he protested.

"Sir Charles Montague," I said quietly, "for I suppose you are the young man the Earl warned would follow me across the seas in jealous rage; there is no cause for your ill-feeling. The Princess considers me even less than she may you."

"That would be mighty little, by George!" he replied with a sigh.

I took pity on the burning passion of the young lover, and so briefly related the circumstances of my acquaintanceship with the Princess.

His anger allayed and his jealousy disarmed, he

humbly apologized for his abruptness and then inquired:

"What is this indigo matter of which you speak?"

"Come, I will show you," and I led the way to my plantation, where in one corner of a field I had had a patch of bushy, blue-green plants, with long narrow leaves and yellow flowers planted.

"Indigo plants," I said, nodding toward them. "Look!"

Gathering several of their leaves, I threw them into a nearby vat where already some were fermenting. As I stirred them up I called his attention to the purple-blue water; then as it settled, I allowed the water to run off from the low-placed spigot. At the bottom of the cask there remained deposits of insoluble indigo.

He nodded appreciatively, as I scraped the mud into a tray. Then, by rapid heating, I produced beautiful purple crystals.

"The Indians' color-dye!" I remarked. "I am more interested in the revival of this industry than in all the princesses of Europe!"

" 'Tis wonderful," he remarked, "and I see no reason why it should not succeed." After a few moments' silence, he added, "If you need money and value not the Princess' ring, I would willingly purchase it at a sum far above its value."

"No, Sir Charles, I do not think that would be courteous toward the lady; but I'll offer the ring as security for a loan to enable me to prove on a large scale that my convictions are practical."

"I accept it," he cried, and as I gave him the ring he passionately kissed the topaz. Then he said, "I am wealthy and carry great influence through the Earl, my kinsman. Maybe I can help you."

Thus we parted. The foundation of my success was laid, for by his influence, a company was formed and stock sold, and the production and sale of indigo from our "Jews' land" increased enormously.

There came a day, however, when tears came into the eyes of the love-stricken man. While his squadron still patrolled the coast, a message came from England, bearing the news of the marriage of the Princess Charlotte to His Majesty King George III.

I put my arm in silent sympathy around his shoulder, we being now firm friends. Then, like the brave man he was, he braced himself and, taking from his finger the topaz ring, he looked at its golden light with dimmed eyes.

"Long live the Queen," he suddenly cried. "I go to offer her friendship and wish her success."

With a sigh he handed me the ring, which we had never referred to since he had received it from me.

"Will you carry it to the Queen," I asked, "as a token of my loyal friendship and wishes for the success of that virtuous and noble lady's reign?"

Silently he nodded his assent.

❖   ❖   ❖

It was another foggy "Guy Fawkes' Day" in London, and the young Queen was holding an informal birthday party at the exclusive Chit Chat Club when Sir Charles, with a gallant air, presented my little indigo-colored plush box.

The lid flew open at the slight pressure of her fingers, revealing to her dancing eyes the largest yellow topaz I could find in the thirteen colonies, its brilliant crystal preserving forever the golden sunshine of South Carolina.

With an exclamation of delight, she lifted the massive jewel; beneath it lay her tiny ring with my message:

"Having brought friendship and success to him to whom you lent it, its service is o'er. I now return it with humble friendship and loyal wishes for the felicity of your reign."

Glancing up, she met Sir Charles' longing, devouring eyes. "It has returned to me at an opportune moment," she said. "Come, Sir Charles, Governor of South Carolina, pray put forth your finger. This shall be my birthday gift and appointment."

He knelt before her and kissed the silken edge of her robe. Then swiftly rising, he cried, "Long live the Queen!"

The cry was taken up by the brilliant company, and none hailed her louder than did a young man of twenty-three who stood by her side, an amused spectator of the little presentation—King George III.

"And Moses Lindo," he added smilingly, "shall be my surveyor and inspector of indigo, drugs, and dyes for the Carolina provinces, and shall forever have the privilege of using my royal coat of arms over his door."

Then the music, hidden in the palm-filled alcove, struck up the strains of *God Save the King*.

The ring of the little Princess had fulfilled its message of friendship. Success beyond measure had been my reward, and South Carolina thus became famous for the indigo plantations of Moses Lindo, the Jew.

"Some row up, but we row down,
All the way to Newport town.
Pull away, pull away!"

"ANOTHER cup of coffee, Sarah," said Aaron Lopez, handing his cup to his daughter, "and then I'll go down to the Long Wharf and bid my new ship godspeed on its maiden voyage."

The soft pink cheeks of the remarkably pretty girl dimpled into smiles as her father playfully tipped her under the chin.

"And if Isaac Elizah and his son call, I want you to give them good welcome. The father is a dear friend, and young Jacob will be a smart lawyer some day. We should encourage their visits." He looked at his daughter shrewdly.

A frown passed over the pretty face. Under the long, silky lashes a pair of dark eyes flashed. The girl, however, made no comment as, absorbed in her thoughts, she poured out her father's coffee.

"Well, Cato!" said the master of the house genially a few minutes later as one of his black servants began to remove the dishes. "How are things this fine summer's morning?"

"Dere's a very rough sea, sir," replied the darky shaking his head gravely. "A very rough sea."

"I'll take a look from the look-out," said his master.

Leaving the breakfast room, he strode up the wide central stairway. Passing through his own room on the third floor he stepped out on to a wooden platform.

Most of the houses on the Mall facing the harbor were of the same type, solid, three-story square buildings as stoutly timbered as though they themselves were ships.

Each house bore on the ridge-pole of its hipped roof a railed platform called "the bridge," whence the watcher could look far out to sea and scan the horizon for incoming and outgoing ships.

Aaron Lopez owned two of these houses, side by side. One was his beautiful home, the other had been made over into counting-house, offices, and sail-loft for storing spare canvas. Attached to this building was a very long, wide wharf.

With a sweeping glance around the wide bay studded with pretty green islets, Aaron Lopez' keen glance took in every type of vessel—merchant ships, whaling brigs, schooners, fishing sloops, small coasting vessels, innumerable rowboats, and similar craft.

His eyes came to rest with kindling pride upon the *Pride of Newport*, a stately three-masted ship moored to the nearby wharf. This towering mass of sails, glistening like snow in the sunshine, was his newest ship, fresh from the shipyards at Bull's Point.

Of a new and daring design, the *Pride of Newport*, a long, sharp, clipper-built craft, was expected to show her heels to almost anything afloat. In a few hours she would slip her cables and sail away to the Spanish main and the far Southern countries beyond.

Aaron Lopez remained for a long time deep in thought. His wife, whom he had brought from Portugal eleven years before with their young daughter, had recently died. Now, more than ever, the bereaved man was passionately drawn toward the sweet girl in whom his beloved wife and mother again lived.

This man, Newport's outstanding merchant and owner of a score of deep water ships and five times as many coasting vessels, was justifiably proud. Proud of his race and ancestry, proud of his business acumen, wealth and influence, proud of his beautiful daughter. And upon this light-hearted, happy young girl was centered all his love, his wealth, and his social ambitions.

His meditations upon these things were suddenly interrupted by the rollicking song of a young fisher-man:

"It's oh! As I was walking out,
   One morning in July,
I met a maid who asked my trade.
 'A flatboatman,' said I
   'From Newport town.' "

"Young Nathan De Leon seems to be always in this neighborhood these days," muttered Aaron Lopez looking down at the beach below. "I wonder why?"

A few minutes later, dressed in lavender-colored silk, his suit trimmed with white lace ruffles at neck and sleeves, and with a new three-cornered beaver hat surmounting his wig of powdered white hair, Aaron Lopez strolled down Thames Street.

The tall, manly merchant-prince of that fair seaport town swung his gold headed walking-stick jauntily, for to him this sailing day was a holiday, the sailing of his first clipper ship.

Into the busy shipping district known as the Points, amid shipyards, from whence came the merry sound of busy hammers, past odoriferous tanneries and distilleries, lengthy rope-walks, and sugar refineries, the shipmaster strolled.

The talk he heard on the narrow streets was of the sea, of big catches, of the price of whale oil, molasses, rum and sugar, and the endless gossip of ships and sailors.

He was compelled to slow his steps in order to avoid stumbling over the discarded litter of the sea— weatherworn blocks and tackle, rusty chains and anchors, empty hogsheads and barrels, dank cordage and broken spars and sea-gear of every description.

Scurrying amid this wreckage were innumerable crabs seeking to escape the bewildering turmoil and regain the peacefulness of their native element.

Over all hovered an aroma of rum, fish, sea salt, hemp and tar, fondly called "sea air" by the good people of the busy little town.

Even the children grew up in the ways of the sea, for on a doorstep of the new synagogue black-eyed little Rachel Nunez was lisping, as she pointed a tiny finger-tip into a New England primer:

> "Whales in the sea
> Their Lord obey."

Outside a coffee-house two sea captains were heatedly debating the differing virtues of brigantine versus barquentine, when, on stepping back, the smallest man of the two, a broad-shouldered, squat little Jew in rough sea garb, unwittingly brushed against the fine clothes of Aaron Lopez.

Immediately, with a change of voice, he broke into profuse apologies, and then, "Why, by the lord Harry, it's our old friend the Commodore himself!" To a certain select few Aaron was known by this honorary title, respectfully given.

"Ah, friend Isaac!" said the "Commodore" good-humoredly. "How now? Still arguing! What a pugnacious little man you are, to be sure!"

"I'm not arguing," protested Isaac De Leon. "I'm

just telling this dumb Englishman something. But say, now, Commodore, is your new-fangled contraption really going to sail?"

Aaron, with a wary eye, nodded.

"But listen here!" continued the persistent red-faced little captain. "Surely, you're not going to let that ship go out to the open sea with all that sail on, even if the wind is favorable."

"Why not?" said Aaron.

"I've told you before and I tell you again," Captain Isaac De Leon shouted with rising irascibility, "she's over-rigged and top-heavy! No ship living can carry all them there sails in a storm or heavy seas. 'Sides, you'll need a battleship's complement of sailors to handle them, and that'll cut into your profits."

"That's what I say," said Captain Howard of the *Greyhound*, an English naval vessel calling in at Newport on customs' duty. "I saw her on her trials as we came in. Fine lines! Trim model! I like her tapering masts, the taut cordage and the swiftness with which she comes about. Ah, she's beautiful both in hull and rigging, and light as a sea-gull—but terribly top-heavy! Safety sacrificed for speed, sir!"

"That's what your own captains say, Commodore; but I won't mention names," added Isaac De Leon, cocking his eye.

"Don't need to," snapped Aaron. "This ship puts all my others in the shade, and though the last two brigs I launched, the *Prudent Sarah* and the *Faithful Abi-*

gail, were fine ships, they won't be in the running with this new model. Certain of my captains, therefore, have their noses out of joint!"

"But, hark ye, Commodore," cried Isaac catching his friend by his ruffled sleeve, "and I'm telling you— all the authorities say ——"

"Drat the authorities!" exclaimed Aaron peevishly, brushing off the restraining hand.

"But look ye here, Aaron! You've never commanded a ship in your life, and ——"

"Go to, now!" exclaimed the exasperated shipmaster. "Am I to be whip-snapped by the captain of a glorified clam-chaser every time we meet?" Captain De Leon was owner and master of the little dingy, patched-sailed, forty-ton coasting vessel *Gloria.*

"Your masts are too high," said Isaac, ignoring the Commodore's outburst. "There's too great a spread of canvas, and square sails, at that."

"A square sail will carry more wind than a triangular one," interrupted Aaron impatiently. "Any fool knows that!"

"Yes, I know," said Isaac without thinking. "But this is only the beginning. You'll be adding side sails, and above the top-gallant royals you'll be putting skysails and moonrakers, and ——"

The crowd of seafaring men who had gathered around laughed.

Aaron flushed with annoyance. "Everything has

been carefully worked out," he said stiffly. "This ship will clip time from every voyage and ——"

"It won't work!" said Isaac wagging his huge head of shaggy hair. "You wait and see! No ship will ever beat the good old brigs that built up Newport's trade and made your name known and respected in every port on both sides of the ocean."

A murmur of approval swept the crowd.

"Well, we'll see," said the somewhat mollified Commodore as he nodded farewell to Isaac, who, though a friend and fellow member of Newport's Jewish Club, was a constant "thorn in the flesh" to Aaron.

"You ought to see the boat my boy has built," remarked Isaac, who, having no notion of being dismissed, was now trotting along by Aaron's side. The little man's eyes glistened with enthusiasm beneath their shaggy, black brows.

"If it's anything like yours—" began the Commodore glancing down at Isaac with a sly smile.

"Oh, no, no!" cried Isaac hastily. "My *Gloria* is an old tub that's seen its best days and has served me well, but Nathan's—ah!" He clasped his hands and wrung them in ecstasy.

"What's this?" cried the Commodore quizzically. "Competition?"

"Maybe—some day!"

"Umph! What shipyard has turned it out?"

"He made it himself, out of his own head," explained Isaac with a wave of his hand.

The Commodore appeared aghast at this apparent miracle. "His own head!" he repeated slowly with twinkling eyes.

"I mean, my boy, my Nathan, he made it during the last two winters and launched it in the cove at our farm. We had good luck in our last summer's trading along the coast in the *Gloria* and that paid for the paint and cordage and the shaping of the planks by the sawmill. Nathan even shaped the ironwork at his own forge."

"So as to evade the English law that forbids us colonists to make nails or bolts."

Isaac nodded. "That's so, Aaron. And now we have two ships. Look to your laurels, Commodore!" He laughed gaily.

Aaron snorted in disgust. Then his face broke into smiles as a well-known, much be-ribboned blue dress and a broad-brimmed straw hat appeared at the entrance to the long wharf just before them. "There's my daughter!" he cried.

"And there's my son, too!" Isaac's eyes sparkled as he pointed to a small, two-masted fishing boat that was skimming over the bay, handled very expertly by a curly-haired young Adonis in leather sea-boots and fisherman's clothes.

Sarah Lopez, who was accompanied by young Jacob Elizah, glanced over the edge of the wharf at the youth and smiled.

Nathan grinned up at the girl and waved his free

hand. His other hand was on the tiller as, with a graceful sweep that barely made a ripple on the water, he brought his fishing boat to a perfect moorage by the side of the long wharf.

"Come away, Miss Lopez," said Jacob Elizah, his swarthy face growing darker as he glanced superciliously at the boat. "Come! Here's your father."

Aaron Lopez, stately and proud, was walking toward them, the gesticulating Captain Isaac De Leon at his side volubly pointing out, with both hands, special features of his son's new boat to the uninterested Commodore—the tiny cabin—the galley, a little box of a place directly behind the mainmast, and the row of fish-bins in which sea water swished and swirled.

"Is your big ship all ready to leave, Father?" asked Sarah.

"Yes, my dear. And some of these clam-boats are likely to get swamped in her backwash if they're not careful," he added, grimly.

"Ha, ha!" laughed Isaac De Leon. "No fear of that. Did you notice how skilfully my boy— Howdy do, Miss Sarah?" he added, breaking off as their eyes met, "and you, too, Jacob."

The young lawyer, stiff and formal, dressed in somber-hued clothes, bowed. He appeared rather out of place on this festive occasion.

Young Nathan had quickly clambered up the rough side of the wharf. He bowed with natural grace to Aaron Lopez and smiled down at his diminutive father. His eyes sparkled so admiringly at Sarah, however, that the girl, blushing slightly, found it necessary to focus her attention upon the *Pride of Newport*.

"It's over-rigged, smothered in sails, Miss Sarah," said Isaac De Leon, following her rapt glance.

"You said that before," remarked Aaron shortly.

"And I'll say it again!" replied Isaac snappily. "It's over-rigged!"

"I think so, too, sir," said Nathan respectfully.

"Oh, you do, do you?" said Aaron sharply. "Now that you're a full-fledged shipbuilder, I s'pose you two fish-peddlers are authorities upon all matters of the sea!

"Why, this tub you've just cut out with a jackknife will never reach deep water," continued Aaron warmly. " 'Tis only fit for sliding over sandbanks and mudflats for mackerel—summer fishing!"

"That's just it, sir!" said Nathan boldly. "It's a mackerel fisher, one of the crankiest boats to handle. Needs more skill to manage than this big windjammer.

"True, sir, the mackerel is a summer fish, coming in the spring and working its way northward until fall when it disappears from the Labrador coast and cannot be found in winter like the cod and halibut.

"But mackerel fishing has dangers all its own, sir. Dangers more menacing than those of the deep sea.

For it is pursued close to shore, in shallow water, where the sand lies a scant two fathoms below the surface, and a southeast wind will, in a few minutes, raise a roaring sea that will pound the stoutest vessel to bits against the bottom."

"I hate the sea!" cried Sarah with an outburst of sudden and unusual vehemence in the presence of male friends. "Fine ships like these, splendid sailors ——"

"Like my son, Nathan," murmured Isaac De Leon.

"—sail away, never to return," continued the young girl. "The deadly toll of the sea is awful. There's hardly a family in Newport without its tragic story of loved ones taken by the cruel sea.

"I remember, for I was but seven years old when we came across the great Atlantic, the terrible storms, the fear of pirates, that awful waste of waters, the icebergs. How frightened I was! It has left me with a great fear of the sea, and so I have kept my father from going to sea, for I knew it would claim him for its own—it is so cruel!"

"But you may yet marry a sailor," said Nathan with a smile, "and forget all your fears of the ocean."

"Never!" cried Sarah with flashing eyes and a determined stamp of her little foot. "None of my loved ones will ever sail the seas—I would lose them; of that I am certain."

"You are wise, Miss Lopez," murmured Jacob Elizah. "Life is safer on *terra firma*."

"Me and my little boy Nathan," interrupted Isaac De Leon, "were in Lisbon in 1755 when it was, in the twinkling of an eye, utterly destroyed by an earth-quake and thirty thousand poor wretches living on solid ground were destroyed. We fled and came in safety by the sea to Newport, the sole survivors of our once happy family." His voice quavered. There was a respectful silence.

"What is the name of your new boat?" asked Aaron turning to Nathan.

"The *Sarah*," said the young man looking out to sea.

The Commodore started. "The *Sarah*!" he exclaimed with a frown.

"Yes, sir; the name of my future wife, I hope."

"What do you mean, sirrah!" snapped the aroused Commodore. "Do you dare to infer? Come, Sarah," he said, at a sudden loss for words. "We must go; our friends at the ship await us."

"I think that fellow is the most impertinent rascal!" exploded the Commodore as they reached the deck of the *Pride of Newport*.

"So do I," said Jacob Elizah, with a quick glance at Sarah. "I would break with that family, sir, if I were you—forbid them the house."

"I have never forbidden any man the hospitality of my home yet," said Aaron Lopez, "but these men, father and son ——"

"Nathan spoke very respectfully, Father," interrupted Sarah softly.

"He was insolent!" said Aaron sharply.

The girl sighed.

A few moments later the little party was enjoying the thrill of congratulations from a select group in the main cabin of the stately vessel.

Then followed a well-served noonday meal, a select dinner attended by Aaron's most personal friends, including Dr. Ezra Stiles, the president of Yale College; Dr. Isaac Touro, the young rabbi of Newport; Isaac and Jacob Elizah, and a few others. On the deck above them fife and fiddle drove away, temporarily, at least, all unpleasant thoughts.

* * *

During the weeks that followed, Isaac Elizah and his son were frequent visitors at Aaron Lopez' beautiful home. But while Sarah was obedient to her father's wishes and made the guests welcome, all three men were somewhat puzzled at the failure of their efforts to weld Sarah's and Jacob's friendship into something deeper and more significant.

So that summer and fall passed; winter was at hand.

"That young Nathan De Leon is in our neighborhood a great deal lately," said Aaron to his daughter one evening. He had heard a manly voice singing:

> "Some row up, but we row down,
> All the way to Newport town,
> Pull away, pull away!"

and upon looking out of the window he had seen the young sailor mending nets on the beach nearby.

"And I've seen him at our door more than once."

"Yes," said Sarah innocently.

"What does he come for?" asked her father, glancing at his daughter suspiciously.

"Dinah buys farm produce, fruits, and vegetables, and sometimes fish, too, from him," replied Sarah with quite an unnecessary blush.

"Well, do we have to buy those things from him?" said Aaron tartly. "Is he the only peddler in Newport?"

"Dinah says ——"

"Dinah does what you tell her," replied Aaron sharply. "So don't try to deceive me, miss."

"I'm sure I'm not trying to deceive you," said Sarah. "You know, Father, I always try to please—" A fine cambric handkerchief came to light to wipe away a few tears.

The great Aaron Lopez, whose word was law to many hundreds of rough toilers of the sea, capitulated at once.

"There, my dear, I did not mean ——"

But his daughter had fled to her room.

The Commodore folded the Newport *Mercury* and propped it up against the coffee pot. He sighed deeply. Things were not going the way he wished. Young Jacob Elizah had made but little progress in the courtship of his daughter, while, on the other hand, young Nathan De Leon appeared altogether too often in his neighborhood.

While there was no lack of respect on the part of the young fisherman, there was a merry twinkle in the eyes of that youth and a quiet spirit of determination about him that annoyed the Commodore considerably.

This was the state of affairs when the great storm that was remembered for many years afterwards, took place one winter's night.

It began with a strong southeast gale which rapidly increased to a violent tempest, and the waves off Point Judith that were always high became truly mountainous in the raging wind.

By nightfall the thunder and lightning, the wind and the rain had reached their greatest intensity. Huge waves were breaking upon the shore, sending clouds of spray into the adjacent streets.

Everything in the town and harbor had been made shipshape in order to contend with the storm; but many were the watchers who peered out into the darkness, seeking, between the flashes of vivid lightning, some evidence of the many ships that were known to be nearing port.

One of these watchers was Aaron Lopez, who, from the look-out gallery of his house, scanned with his telescope the heaving waters on the horizon during the constant play of the lightning.

That afternoon news had come by carrier-pigeon

that the *Pride of Newport*, after a record-breaking voyage, had been seen off the coast of Long Island, crowding on every sail in order to reach her home port before the storm reached its height.

A light touch upon his arm aroused him from his intense concentration. It was Sarah.

The girl brushed back the thick curls tossing in front of her eyes and seized his arm in an agony of fear. "Oh, I'm so afraid!" she cried. Her words were lost in the storm.

The father passed a comforting arm around his daughter's shoulders and pressed her to his side.

Standing side by side, silent because of the turmoil, and somewhat sheltered by the woodwork, they scanned the tossing water with its raging breakers.

Suddenly the girl felt her father tremble. She looked inquiringly up into his face and then, looking out to sea, she saw, outlined by lightning, the form of a great ship under bare masts tossing like a shuttlecock on the far distant waters. The ship was evidently seeking to work its way off again through the gale to the safety of the open sea.

Aaron's anxious face was pale and stern. Sarah clung to his arm. They silently watched the *Pride of Newport* drifting ever closer, struggling to avoid the treacherous line of rocks fringing Newport Bay. But the buffeting the big ship was receiving made that very difficult. Probably her anchors were dragging.

The news of the great ship's dilemma was now

known to all. Along the shore line seafaring men with their womenfolk, many of whom had loved ones aboard the drifting vessel, were talking in anxious little groups.

"Wrap up in bonnet and shawl," yelled Aaron, above the howling wind, to his daughter, "and we'll go down to the beach. 'Tis a losing battle, I'm afraid."

" 'Tis too bad, Commodore," shouted a voice in the dark, "that the homecoming of your fine ship should be so tragic."

Turning sharply, Aaron looked down into a hooded oilskin cowl and recognized the voice as that of Isaac De Leon.

"Umph!" he grunted. " 'Tis not the ship I'm thinking of, but the brave souls aboard her.

"God save them!" he added, for, at that moment, the *Pride of Newport* was brought up suddenly and violently; she had struck the rocks. Then, trembling for a few seconds like a leaf, she keeled over at a sharp angle and remained fast.

"Where's Peleg Folger, the whaler?" cried Aaron. "He's our best harpoon-thrower."

"Here, sir," shouted a gruff voice. "Right by ye."

"Get to the nearest point on the cliffs. The ship's not far out. See if you can throw a rope over her."

Within a few minutes, a great crowd had gathered at the significantly named Foul Bay, the nearest point to the rocks on which the *Pride of Newport* lay.

From a huge jutting rock the expert harpooner cast his weapon with a light rope attached, hoping that it would go over the wreck and enable the crew to haul it in and thus make connection with the shore. If only he could do this, the men would have a fighting chance to save their lives.

Again and again the sturdy whaler cast, but the wind swept the harpoon far from its objective.

Involuntary sobs came from the throats of the anxious onlookers as it became increasingly evident that nothing could be done.

Foul Bay, a wide and shallow portion of the spacious harbor, consisted of shifting sand, a little more than two fathoms deep. The hidden rocks upon which the ship had struck fringed this shallow area.

A sudden thought struck Nathan. "My sloop!" he cried. "I believe I could make it, sir," he added, turning to Aaron.

"Nonsense, boy! No boat could ——"

Nathan, however, had disappeared.

Meanwhile the raging breakers were pounding the great ship on the jagged edges of the rocks. The crew, clad in oilskins, could be seen clinging to the rigging, with their pale, white faces turned to their friends upon the shore.

Then from a sheltered cove less than a quarter of a mile away, a long, slim boat darted upon the raging waters. Its small sail was rigged slantingly so as to enable the little boat to zigzag through the wind

186

that was blowing almost directly on to the shore.

In a sudden blinding flash of lightning the solitary figure at the helm of the sloop stood revealed, Nathan De Leon.

With infinite skill he guided what appeared to be a mere chip on the bubbling, swirling eddies over the great rolling breakers. As he worked his boat in a cautious, slanting direction toward the wreck, one could see the breakers under its bows showing white through the darkness like the fangs of a savage beast.

Then came a wild cry, heard even above the storm, "Nathan, my boy, come back! Oh, Nathan!"

Aaron Lopez passed a protecting arm around the trembling shoulders of Isaac De Leon, while Sarah, her face pale in silent agony, strove through staring eyes to follow the flimsy sloop as it outrode the wild, cruel waves.

"There goes the mainmast!" cried a dozen watchers in unison as, bent and twisted by the tempestuous wind, the overstrained pole of the *Pride of Newport* went by the board and splashed into the sea. A moment later a second mast also snapped with a sharp crack that was plainly heard.

Then the ship righted itself with a sudden lurch, plunged forward and sank into deeper water until the main deck, at an acute angle, was awash.

"The mackerel boat!" cried several. "Where is she?"

There was a tense silence. Not a word was uttered. Nathan's tiny vessel was nowhere to be seen.

Then a glad cry of relief arose. From behind a huge wave, out into a whirlpool of dark, eddying water, floated the boat like a buoyant cork. Its tiny triangular sail fluttered wildly as the young sailor calmly manipulated the helm.

Nathan De Leon had put so much of his talent into his little fishing boat that it had become part and parcel of himself. Taking advantage of every gust of wind and calling upon all his knowledge of the sea, he traveled a most erratic course and missed disaster time and time again by a mere hair's breadth. Thus he slowly approached the wreck.

Again his boat was hidden from sight by the sheets of driving rain, spray and wind-driven mist.

For several minutes the waiting crowds remained silent in dreadful anxiety, and then a shout of joy went up. Nathan was returning. Dark figures lay huddled on the deck of his little vessel.

As soon as he neared the shore, Nathan waved a greeting. In his hand he held a rope that evidently reached from the wreck to the shore.

Wild shouts of acclaim greeted him as his gallant boat grounded on the beach. A score of hands seized him in frantic embrace.

His father, almost speechless, jumped up and down in delirious excitement. "Nathan, my Nathan! My brave boy!" he cried hysterically.

Many willing hands were now aiding in rescuing the crew. By means of a pair of canvas breeches secured to a lifebuoy traveling on a life-line to the ship's mast, the sailors were hauled to shore.

"Nathan!" said Aaron Lopez seizing the hand of the young Jew and shaking it with deep emotion. "You are a hero! I'm proud of you; we all are!"

"I'm sorry 'bout the *Pride of Newport*, sir," said Nathan, looking sadly at the spot where the once fine vessel now lay on the cruel rocks.

"I care naught for the ship, just so that my brave men are safe. My losses can easily be repaired," said Aaron. "But, Nathan, you and your boat constitute the pride of Newport now!"

"Aye, that's so!" interrupted the beaming Isaac De Leon.

"I think Nathan should change the name of his vessel to the *Pride of Newport*, if you have no objection, Father," said Sarah with soft, sparkling eyes.

The nervous young man in front of her shifted his feet at a loss for words.

"But I do object," said Aaron loudly, but with a merry twinkle in his eyes. "I think its present name should remain."

Nathan looked at Aaron Lopez in quick surprise.

"The *Sarah*?" asked Isaac De Leon, perplexedly wrinkling his brows.

"He understands," replied the shipmaster smiling.

Nathan nodded happily while Sarah became suddenly intent upon the saving of the crew of the *Pride of Newport*.

WILLIAM TRYON, Governor, Captain-General, Commander-in-Chief, and Vice-Admiral of His Britannic Majesty's province of North Carolina, was a happy man.

The bright sunshine of a May morning in the year 1771 reflected the beauty of his scarlet, gold-laced uniform as he stood by the river bank admiring his new palace, the most magnificent mansion in all the thirteen colonies.

The little capital of the colony, New Berne, half-hidden amidst the fresh young foliage and blossoms of spring, encircled the palace, a three-storied main building of brick and marble. The building was also a reproduction of "My Lord Mayor of London's" Mansion House, and was connected with two-storied side buildings by graceful, curving galleries.

The scaffolding and litter of several years' building

operations had been removed by the many skilled European artisans and the full grandeur of the palace, surrounded by spacious lawns, stood revealed— graceful Ionic columns, statuary, ornamental scrollwork and fountains. It was a picture of which all the Governor's colonial subjects should be proud.

So thought the happy Tryon advancing to meet "Her Excellency," his wife, a shy, quiet little lady whose sad, reflective eyes seemed ever to long for far-away England.

"Ah, my dear," he said proudly, "it is finished at last—the finest mansion in all this American wilderness. Our good subjects are highly honored this day. Come! Read Sir William's eulogy."

Over the main door appeared the armoral bearings of the Governor, under which, on a richly ornamental marble tablet, a eulogy began:

> "In the reign of a monarch whose
> goodness disclosed
> A free, happy people ——"

But the loyal sentiments ceased, for a young man whose head of black, curly hair bobbed up and down in the intensity of his labors, was busily pasting over the remaining words a placard, on which the words

> "—to dread tyrants opposed,"

stood out in bold, black lettering, while King George and his Queen frowned their disapproval from nearby medallions.

The Governor, puffing up like one of the numerous pouter pigeons on his lawns, swayed with anger.

Ignoring the light touch of his wife's restraining hand, he seized the young man, who was so intent on his work that he did not hear the Governor's approach, by the shoulder, and tore the offensive placard from the marble tablet.

"More Regulators' work," the Governor stormed, pointing to the signature, "R."

"Scurvy ingrates," he continued, "daring to band together and refusing to pay taxes to their King! Behold! Here is a public ornament, a credit to the province and an honor to British America for all time, and you discontented miscreants deface it."

The young man appeared not in the least disturbed. "Five hundred thousand dollars of the people's money thus squandered," he said, waving his hand toward the palace. "Next you'll want a golden throne and a body-guard dressed like this," and he gave the tasseled ends of the Governor's silken sash a playful tug.

"Here, Hawks!" the Governor called to a man passing by the foot of the marble steps. "Who is this person?"

John Hawks, superintendent of construction, peered into the face of the stranger. "Really, Your Excellency, I cannot tell you. There are so many, but wait! I think he brought a shipment of fur rugs from the Philadelphia Jews who trade with the Indians."

"Jail him while I investigate," the Governor ordered. "This action savors of rebellion, and 'twill go hard with the Jews if they countenance such disloyalty."

The first evidence of fear could be seen in the eyes of the young Jew—fear lest others should suffer through his actions. Laying one hand on the marble balcony, he suddenly leaped over it and swiftly disappeared in the shrubbery.

Governor William Tryon strode into his library and threw himself into the welcoming arms of one of his richly upholstered chairs.

Only that morning his private agent had warned him that the people were rebelling against excessive taxation, extortionate fees and the oppressive manner of collecting them, the insolent sheriffs, the picked juries, and the corrupt courts.

After a few moments he banged his fist on the desk before him. "By George!" he roared.

"Regulators, indeed! I'll regulate them! Every day I hear their mutinous mutterings."

Thus aroused, he stepped to one of the French windows and looked out over river, pine forest, and rolling countryside, and decided to levy more taxes. The yachting, horse-racing, and fox-hunting of England should be introduced, and New Berne made the center of social life and gaiety.

Little did he realize that a great storm was brewing which would within ten years sweep away every

He leaped over the marble balcony.

vestige of royal rule from the thirteen colonies, laying his palace in ashes, while its royal Governor fled in terror to the protection of a British frigate.

A sharp knock on the door and an officer of the militia stepped in. "We captured the Jew," he announced, "but barely had time to learn that his name was Jacob Henry before a mob of Regulators rescued him from our hands. More than that, they seized and destroyed our ammunition, while many of my men deserted, taking their weapons with them."

The Governor's face clouded. "Go," he commanded; "I will see you later."

He was now hearing the growling of the backwoods. Thousands of settlers had been pouring into the more fertile valleys inland from the coast during the past few years and they were not disposed quietly to bear injustice. They intended, they said, to regulate the affairs of the colony for the benefit of the people and not as the King's representative desired to do, on the "Grand Model" laid down by John Locke, England's great philosopher. They did not want the colony ruled by a grand seignior, barons and feudal courts, with the tenants as serfs, and slaves at the absolute will of their masters.

The Governor sighed as he thought of what might have been. Then he decided ruthlessly to crush the spirit of revolt even as he had crushed the Cherokee Indians until in terror they called him "the Great Wolf of North Carolina."

Tonight, however, the landed gentry, the little up-start society of New Berne, were to be his guests at the grand "house-warming" ball of his new palace. Even now, friends from afar were arriving by post-chaise with light heart and merry laughter, for little did high rank and society heed the threatening murmurs of the common people.

In the midst of a stately quadrille that night, how-ever, when all was forgotten save the glory of the Governor's ball, there came the crash of leaded glass and a figure, half naked, bruised and bleeding, smothered from head to foot in tar that dripped on fair dresses and bright uniforms, fell into the room through a shattered window casement.

Colonel Edmund Fanning, the Governor's chief extortioner, whose harsh methods had made him the special object of the people's enmity, sprawled over the floor, a pitiable sight.

Briefly he told his story. How the Regulators, breaking camp in the hills, had swooped down on Hillsborough settlement. Mocking what they called the travesty of justice administered by Judge Hen-derson, they had driven the judge and others from the court. Fanning's house had been destroyed by the enraged people who were now marching on the capital.

At this news the Governor's ball broke up in a panic. Hastily the authorities prepared for defense, but, having the royal troops, little fear was felt by the Governor and the Council. The Regulators would be stopped from rapine and destruction.

It was Jacob Henry, however, who stopped them. As the aroused farmers, Indian traders, backwoodsmen, settlers, and others hastened through the great pine forests, gathering momentum as they swept toward the little capital on vengeance bent, the cooler, wiser heads sought to stem the angry torrent of passion-filled men, women and boys. Hermon Husband, their leader, was listened to with scant patience, for, as a Quaker, the mob, while admiring his intelligence, despised him for his pacifism.

Jacob Henry, from the top of a great rock, looked down upon a weird sight as the red, smoky glare of innumerable pine torches lit up the faces and figures of the surging crowds. Some were disguised as Indians. Some had blackened their faces. Others were clad in the fringed deer-skins of frontiersmen or the uniforms of the militia. And amidst them all, shrieking women and shouting boys ran to and fro adding to the din and confusion.

"Back to Regulation Camp!" Jacob urged. "Let's drill and train so that we can better meet our enemy." Hermon Husband and others also pleaded for order and discipline, but the maddened crowds, urged on by James Few, their fanatical leader, hastened on.

It was only when thoughts of the Royal Artillery sobered them, and brave Hermon Husband offered to plead as their representative with the Governor on their behalf, that the Regulators heeded Jacob and halted on the outskirts of New Berne.

Upon Husband's appearance, he was summarily thrown into prison by the infuriated Governor.

Then, the Regulators' ardor having cooled, they sullenly returned to their camp in the hills.

Swiftly the Governor acted. With the might of Empire behind him, his forces moved on the Regulators' camp. With artillery and the advantage of greater military resources he, on the sixteenth of May, 1771, overwhelmed the Regulators on the banks of the Alamance River, and executed those leaders of the revolt he captured.

Jacob Henry, however, escaped capture and with others of like mind bided his time and waited for the ever-increasing discontent to flare up into open revolution in every one of the thirteen colonies, which it did exactly four years later at Lexington in 1775.

* * *

The Revolution was over; but Jacob Henry, gladly welcomed by the people on his return to North Carolina and elected the representative of Carteret County in the State Legislature, found that the struggle for liberty and justice had merely been transferred from the battlefield to the legislative chambers.

Jesse Cooper, New Berne's wealthy caterer to the late royal Governor, opened the battle against Jacob at the first session of the State Legislature.

"Mr. Speaker," he said, "I protest against this wandering Jew coming into our midst once again to trouble us and to take his seat in this House in violation of the Thirty-second Clause of our Constitution, which declares 'that no person who shall deny the truth of the Protestant religion or the Divine authority either of the Old or the New Testament shall be capable of holding any office or place of trust or profit in the civil department within this State.'"

Immediately the Chamber was in an uproar. Some members sided with Cooper, while others voiced their disapproval of the revival of an intolerant clause which had become a dead letter.

During a lull in the heated debate Jacob Henry rose and addressed the Chamber himself:

"If a man should hold religious principles incompatible with the freedom and safety of the State," he said, "I do not hestitate to pronounce that he should be excluded from the public councils of the same, and no one would be more ready to aid and assist than myself. But I should really be at a loss to specify any known religious principles which are thus dangerous. It is surely a question between a man and his Maker, and requires more than human attributes to pronounce which of the numerous sects prevailing in the world is most acceptable to the Deity.

"Shall this now free country set an example of persecution? Will you drive from your shores and from the shelter of your Constitution all those who do not lay their obligations on the same altar, observe the same ritual, and subscribe to the same dogmas?

"The religion I profess inculcates every duty which man owes to his fellow men; it enjoins the practice of every virtue, and the detestation of every vice. This, gentlemen, is my creed.

"Mr. Speaker, I am sure that you cannot see anything in this religion to deprive me of my seat in this House.

"So far as relates to my life and conduct, the examination of these I submit with cheerfulness to your candid and liberal construction.

"No man subscribes more sincerely than myself to the maxim, 'Whatever ye would that men should do unto you, do ye unto them, for such is the law and the prophets.'"

Jacob Henry's speech was received with great applause, but the favorable impression thus made enraged his enemies.

James Smith jumped to his feet, shouting, "We have formed a government for millions who are not yet in existence. In the course of a few hundred years a Jew or Papist might occupy the Governor's chair. Unless we abide by our Constitution, I see nothing against it."

"Bigotry!" cried William Gaston, a Catholic.

"You may call me a bigot as much as you please," replied Smith, "but I am not willing to let in Catholics, Jews, Turks, and heathen. Must we separate the

Holy Scriptures that we may swear this Jew on the Old Testament?"

"God forbid!" added David Caldwell, the Church of England parson, ever fearful lest the newly formed republic should forsake the Established Church. "That would be an invitation for Jews and pagans of every kind to come among us."

"We want no Jews!" Jesse Cooper again shouted. "There never was a Jew yet who wasn't a Shylock, demanding his pound of flesh; ignorers of our Savior, self-seekers, unreliable; yea, cowards ——"

Jesse Cooper's voice had risen almost to a shriek. Then one rose from his seat at whose words all men listened with respect, for he, the friend of Madison and Jefferson, was the coming man of North Carolina, Nathaniel Macon.

"Friends," he began, as Cooper subsided, "if a Hindu were to come among us and were fully qualified to discharge the duties of any office to which he might aspire, his religious beliefs should not constitute an objection for debarment. Who made man a judge that he should presume to interfere with the sacred rights of conscience?

"Alas! Have we just religion enough to hate and not enough to love each other?

"Why are the Jews to be excluded from office? They were the favorite people of the Almighty. Our Savior and his disciples were Jews, and are there not men among the Jews as talented, as virtuous, and as well qualified to fill any office in our Government as any other citizens in our community?

"And loyalty? General Greene, with whom, as you know, I served, did tell me of this man's heroism when, with others of his race, he kept the foe at bay while our retreating artillery passed safely over the Delaware. Then, when Jacob Cohen, his fellow prisoner on the prison-ship, *Torbay*, did show him a way of escape he refused the proffered freedom because Isaacs, their Colonel, was too badly wounded to escape with them. Loyalty? Why prate of loyalty when heroes stand before you?

"Nor did the Jewish merchants of those stirring days prove unreliable, self-seeking men. On the contrary. They aided us with money and with goods. They were among our most active patriots. Of such, for instance, were Michael and Barnard Gratz, of Philadelphia, who struck the first blow at tyranny by signing the Non-Importation Resolutions ——"

"They did?" queried Jacob Henry, springing to his feet in excited amazement.

"Surely—in 1765."

Jacob Henry appeared dazed. "But that was what we quarreled over," he muttered.

"I am Jacob Gratz, their younger brother," he explained. "Considering my elder brothers slow at rebelling against royal pretensions, I, in disgust, came to North Carolina with a shipment of merchandise to Governor Tryon. Then, fearing lest my actions with the Regulators should prove harmful to them in Philadelphia, I have since lived a roaming life under the name of Jacob Henry. Michael and Barnard must have signed the Resolutions after I left, and I have not heard from them since."

Nathaniel Macon continued his interrupted speech. "If any person," he said, "Jew or gentile, notwithstanding their religion, acquire the confidence and esteem of the people of America by their good conduct and practice of virtue, they should not be barred from office in the republic that they helped to save.

"Let us keep strictly to our Constitution, if that is your desire. Let Catholics and Jews be debarred from the *civil* department, if you wish; but let us not violate our Constitution by barring our fellow citizens of those faiths from the *legislative* branch of our State, which is above all civil offices. In other words, non-Protestants can help make our laws, but must neither execute nor interpret them! This is an anomaly which will, in time, rectify itself by its inherent injustice."

His clear, incisive words carried conviction to many a man who was wavering between the bigotry of the past and the spirit of the new era of tolerance ushered in by the Revolution. Therefore, be it said to the honor of North Carolina, Jacob Henry that day took his seat in the Legislature of the state he had helped to save, while his life and example were used in other states to bring about the emancipation of every Jewish citizen in the new republic.

THE JEW

WHO WOULD NOT FIGHT

*Fate Takes a Hand to Change the Life of Jonas
Abram, the Peace-loving Giant*

IF ANYBODY says that I, Jonas Abram, of Hill Bridge
Farm, in Sanbornton settlement, New Hampshire,
farmer and millwright, wrote this account of the
coming of the Revolution, now happily over, to our
little settlement as a matter of personal prowess and
pride, he does me grave injustice.

Nay! It is to straighten out many exaggerated
stories spread by our gossips that I take this opportunity, now that winter storms have stopped all labor
on the farm, of setting down a true account of those
stirring times.

It was on the morning of the twentieth of April in
the year 1775, that our letter-carrier, Ezekiel Moore,
flying past my grist mill on his pony, shouted the
news of the slaughter of Captain John Parker's
minute-men by the British soldiers at Lexington the
previous day.

I made no comment, for I am a man of few words and slow of thought. I had just finished clearing the winter's driftwood from the mill-race and had put on my cardigan jacket, for Sarah, my sister, had brought my dinner and was now sitting on the guard-rail nearby.

The post-carrier's news must have alarmed her, for she suddenly burst into tears.

"What be the matter wi' thee, ye great zany?" I growled. " 'Tis sad news, I trow; but what is it to us? Come, I will walk up to the farm with thee."

I put my arm around her shoulders and we crossed the little bridge of cedar logs that led to my cabin farmhouse.

Sarah continued to sob as we walked along. " 'Tis rebellion against the King," she cried. "It means that you must go and fight."

I laughed aloud, for I was ever a man of peace.

"And dear Samuel, too, will have to go." A passionate flood of tears poured down my sister's pretty cheeks.

"Samuel!" I repeated, puzzled.

Sarah blushed and confusedly sought to escape from my restraining arm.

"You don't mean—?" I stopped and gasped.

My sister nodded. "Samuel Moses and I love each other," she said, with a defiant toss of her head.

"But young Colby," I stammered. "I thought you welcomed his kindly attentions."

"Of course, I greet him kindly. How else should I feel toward such a dear friend? But he is a gentile; we are Jews. I could not love him as I do Samuel."

We walked on in silence until we neared the farm-house door. There we both stopped in surprise. A goodly company of our neighbors were visiting us apparently. A sonorous voice was reading aloud the famous Association Test of our State:

"To show our determination in joining our American brethren and in defending the lives, liberties and properties of the inhabitants of the united colonies, we do hereby solemnly engage and promise that we will, to the utmost of our power, at the risk of our lives and fortunes, with arms, oppose the hostile proceedings of the British fleets and armies against the united American colonies."*

Ebenezer Webster, a tall, ungainly man, dressed in blue homespun, with a complexion dark as an Indian's, his great black eyes shaded by heavy eyebrows, folded the document as we entered. "Welcome, Jonas," he cried, "thou art our champion; wear now thy belt and wrestle with the King of England!"

He referred to my possession of the championship belt, won in fair bout of wrestling from Nathaniel Greene, the blacksmith of Coventry, and unchallenged save by "Red Mike," the Irish giant of the flax-spinners' colony.

* Note—This official document is an exact quotation. See *History of Sanbornton, N. H.,* by Rev. Moses T. Runnels, Boston, 1881.

"My uncle Webster is eloquent," remarked Ebenezer Colby, turning to me. "Indeed, Jonas, the country is aroused. Every road to Boston is alive with angry men; Ethan Allen is bringing the Green Mountain boys; John Stark will lead us; Nathaniel Greene, expelled by the Quakers, is seeking service with Washington. Even old Israel Putnam left his plough in a furrow, and with a flock of sheep is on his way to Cambridge Common. Sign the Test, Jonas, and come with us."

To their amazement I turned and fled. I, the strongest man in the Northern colonies, descendant of Jonas Abram, that ship's carpenter, who with Thomas Webster, the Scotch pioneer, and Richard Putnam, a wild, roving character from England, had built the stockade at the crotch of the rivers.

Why did I flee? I lacked not courage, for unarmed have I faced wolf and bear in defense of my own; and in peril of life itself did I hold back the water-wheel while others saved the silly lambkins swept by flood waters into its spokes. But the sight of blood I cannot abide since the sad day of the schoolhouse massacre when my six little companions, disobeying the dominie's command not to leave the schoolhouse enclosure during the noon-hour recess, had surrendered to the call of the minnow brook and were tomahawked by the savages—as I, too, would have been had I not lingered to examine my torn pantaloons behind the bushes. Even now, when the remembrance of their young lifeblood purpling the green of that drowsy midsummer's day arises before me, fear and a strange nausea overcome me, while my knees tremble as with an ague.

And now "bloody-backs," as the red-coated soldiers of our King were called, were to slay or be slain in this peaceful valley from which the cruel Mohawk has been forever driven.

My reverie by the pool at which I was sitting was broken by the sound of distant firing, while above the garnet-tipped maples and budding willows I saw thin wisps of smoke arising.

Sauntering toward the tumult of distant outcries, I discovered Rufus Putnam's barns in flames, while scattered, smoldering straw on his farmhouse porch was being rapidly stamped out. Rufus, the old gossips say, was the half-brother of Israel Putnam.

"What has happened?" I asked, pressing my way through the gesticulating women around Webster, who was bending over the figure of Colby laid on a grassy patch.

A dozen voices told me that foraging soldiers, in revenge for the old veteran of the French and Indian wars taking up arms against the King, had sought to burn Putnam's farm. Colby on his way home endeavored to rally the farm help, but the trained troops, scattering them and wounding Colby, had fired the farm and had carried off Putnam's pretty niece, Mehetabel.

"Wilt fight now?" demanded Cole Weeks, coming over to me with clenched fists. "The soldiers have taken the sweetest girl in all the colonies. Our 'Queenie' would look at none of us, having eyes only for you, thou big oaf whose dull wit sees not the love-light in a maid's eyes. Speak, man, speak! Art thou dumb?"

I pushed him gently aside. He was unpleasantly near. And I angrily growled, "I'll bring her back." Then, without a word, I strode off in the direction the soldiers had gone.

My mind was in a tumult. I passed groups of marching men, who seemed to envy my swift, swinging stride. I presently saw from a little hill a glimpse of flashing steel, and a moment later discovered the redcoats leisurely resting in a sheltered bend of the Merrimac River.

The girl's foot was fastened to a scrub oak by the chain of the officer's steed. At the insult my strength rose within me. Before the startled men could recover, I was among them, had snapped the chain, and, tossing a trooper over my shoulder by a neat trick known only to wrestlers, was on my way back with the half-fainting girl under my arm.

But it was not to be! Sharp came the word of command, and quickly the men surrounded me. Though I bowled them over like nine-pins, I was overpowered by numbers alone, and soon lay like a trussed fowl, blinking stupidly at the sun.

The officer, twirling his moustache, strolled over and felt my muscles. "By George! Strength and courage personified!" he muttered. "Wilt take the King's shilling?" he asked, after a moment's pause.

"I am no warrior," I growled, "and seek no man's blood."

He laughed and turned to the terror-stricken girl. "Who is this fellow?" he asked.

In her desperation she took an audacious step: "He is my husband," she replied quickly.

"So! Now I understand the reason for his ferocious attack," the officer said, again turning to me. "You did well to come to the rescue of so sweet a wife, for I doubt whether this pretty rebel would have been safe in Boston. Even now," he laughed sardonically.

"If one hair of her head is touched"—I shouted. A cord snapped as I struggled to arise.

"Don't get excited, man!" he replied. "She is safe till we reach Boston, where you had better join your King's army," he added, with a grin.

"I will not!" I said firmly, but sullenly.

So to Boston we went and were imprisoned in a cell in Castle Island fort.

"Thou hast made a pretty mess of things," I growled when we were alone. "And what will be the end of it, I know not!" I turned away in disgust, half-expecting to hear her teasing giggle or receive her witty sally, as was her nature.

To my surprise, she took my scolding as meekly as Nellie, my sheep dog, would have done, looking at me with such beseeching eyes and weeping so sadly that I could do naught but soothe her with promises of early freedom.

Then in came the Rev. Joseph Woodman, the pastor of our settlement, who had been arrested and brought to Boston for having been the first to sign the Test. Released under parole, and hearing of our predicament, he had obtained permission to see us.

"Death may await you, Jonas, for your attack on the soldiers," he said, "unless proof can be shown that you sought to rescue your wife from a fate worse than death; they may also hope to win you to the Loyalists' side."

"Mehetabel is not my wife," I replied.

"But I can perform the ceremony, if you wish," he suggested.

"No, no!" I threw up my hands in alarm at the idea.

He shook his head sadly. The maid sat on the cot, her beautiful eyes full of despair, her face as stony-white as our native granite. My heart was stricken sore.

"What will become of her?" I murmured.

The minister's low whisper aroused my dull mind. "God of Israel forbid!" I cried. "The maid shall be my wife, an' she will." I turned toward the trembling girl, who reeled and would have fallen, had I not caught her in my tingling arms.

A few minutes later the guard threw open the door and we were led before the commander of the prison, a gray-haired veteran whose scarred face and an empty sleeve spoke mutely of warfare's ravages. He glanced at us with stern eyes, consulted his paper and turned to the minister.

"You have been parson of Sanbornton for many years, performing many marriages there; can you vouch that these two are man and wife?"

"I married them," was the quiet reply.

"Umph!" the commandant grunted. He glanced through the window at the swarming hordes of angry men, gathering at the news of Concord. He seemed worried. Suddenly he turned. "You're free," he snapped. "But join the King's army, man! And you, my lassie, tell your uncle, my old friend, Israel Putnam, that a high commission awaits him from his king! Go!"

Thus we returned to Sanbornton, where I found that, marvelous as my adventures had been, stranger events had happened during my absence; for, after the rough surgery of Ebenezer Webster had extracted the bullet from Colby's shoulder and he had drawn a quart or more of blood to ease the wound, as he said, young Colby fell into a rapid and weakening decline from which nothing seemed to arouse him except my sister's presence.

Finally, when all seemed hopeless and the end near, Webster, in his blunt manner, asked my sister if she would marry the stricken man who so evidently adored her.

Samuel Moses, who happened to be in the sick-room at the time, winced with pain, but bravely smiled his approval across the couch to my sister.

Seeing the dull eyes light up with hope, Sarah, smiling her consent, knelt and kissed the wounded man, while her tears fell upon his brow. With our return, the parson married them.

Were ever such strange twists of Fate given to poor human straws on the stream of life as happened to us in the days of the Revolution? Brave Samuel departed with a light step, but heavy heart; while I, lingering over the heavy spring work on my farm, was unhappy over the matter of signing the Test.

It was the urgings of my sweet young wife that settled my uncertainty; and so, I set out at a steady tramp for Concord village.

In the ravine leading from our valley, I met a party of Green Mountain boys coming down from their Londonderry settlement.

" 'Tis the Jew-boy!" cried out their leader, a giant red-haired Irishman, known as "Red Mike." "Bedad —and be ye, too, going to fight the redcoats?"

"I am," I replied. "Can I march with you?"

"No!" roared several of the little company, encouraged by their leader whose challenge for the wrestling championship I had not yet accepted. "We want no money-lending Jews with us."

"Pass on, then," I replied carelessly, sitting down on a boulder and waiting for the score of men and boys to pass.

A stone struck my arm, and as I glanced up, a little lad hurriedly took protection at the side of Red Mike.

"You touch me, and me big brother will murther ye," whimpered the boy, while the Irishman laughed contemptuously.

Pushing aside the intervening men and towering above them all, even their leader, I seized Red Mike by his bright green scarf, shook him fiercely and said, "When this is over, meet me. I'll guarantee to hold the belt against ye and all comers."

" 'Tis well and truly said, man," he spoke respectfully. "Gi'e me your hand on it. After this bally scrap is o'er, bedad, we'll ha'e a friendly bout, e'en though ye be a Jew."

The shortest route to Concord was the Cannonball trail, leading from the iron pockets in the granite hills and the iron mines abandoned since the British ruling that they were a common nuisance. This was the road we took. Coming to a split in the trail, I, with two others, had taken an upper path, looking down on the big Irishman, roaring out a vulgar song, and followed by his fellows picking their way over the rocks.

Then, as Red Mike turned to help his little brother, a sudden volley of musketry came from behind several great boulders, and some of our men fell. The Irishman, stopping abruptly in his song, waved his shillalah, shouting, " 'Tis the enemy! Come on, boys! After the spalpeens!"

But from above the granite boulder behind him appeared an ugly face. An arm reached out and deep in the hero's back a bayonet was plunged. Red Mike sank down never to rise again, while a piercing shriek arose from the little lad kneeling beside him, frantically calling upon the holy saints for help, and a malicious grin swept over the face of the soldier who again raised his weapon.

The sight cleared my stupefied senses. Seizing a granite boulder that six men could not ordinarily have moved, I hurled it down at the head of the soldier. It splintered against the sides of the ravine and scattered the soldiers who, kneeling in the open path, were preparing to fire a volley at our men.

With a wild shout, I sprang down from rock to rock, into the enemy group. Seizing a soldier in each hand I dashed their heads against the boulders. Roaring like a lion, I struck at their colonel, "Ye killed him foul, you brute! Ye killed him foul!" Tears streamed down my face. Then friend and foe fled— afraid—for I felt like a giant bull-elephant raging mad! The Green Mountain boys gathered in a little group at the end of the gully, while, throwing away their equipment and even their weapons, the soldiers fled from the spot.

Torn and covered with blood, I hurried to the fallen Mike. To the wondering, scared group who slowly returned and sought to pacify the screaming lad, I kept muttering: "They killed him foul! foul! foul! Who are they?" I asked, noticing for the first time the soldiers' blue uniforms, as they lay scattered and moaning.

"They spoke German," replied one, and as I glanced at him he turned to flee, so scared were the simple flax-spinners at my angry strength.

"God of Israel!" I ejaculated. "Is the King sending German soldiers to punish his English subjects? That would be beyond all reason. What is this?" I picked up a sealed package in a black leather cover.

"This is the dispatch Red Mike was commissioned to give the commander in Concord," said one.

"Then on to Concord!" I leaped to my feet, and dragging the poor lad away by main force, we hastened toward the village.

The good people of Concord say it was a strange sight to see a ragged, bloody, Indian-like Jew come striding through the streets carrying a little sleeping, tear-stained Irish boy across his shoulder.

So disturbed were my thoughts, so scattered my wits and so angry were my feelings at the foul murder, that the events of those days are blurred in my memory. I know the commandant received me kindly, read the dispatch Red Mike had carried, which proved to be the Test, signed by every man but one in our settlement, and when he commented on my name being absent from it, I signed it with big scrawling letters, not being a man of scholarly attainments, as some of our people are. Then he appointed me captain of the Green Mountain Militia and told me to prepare for the siege of Boston—where poor Colby was to fall in the defense of Bunker Hill, leaving my sister to the loving care of Samuel Moses.

Dazed and bewildered beyond endurance, my simple mind demanded rest, and I fell into a sleep so deep that the little Irish boy thought I would never awake.

After many hours I stirred, and when the memory of the recent tragedy came to mind it grieved me sorely; but, taking courage, I cast off fear like a Newfoundland dog shaking water off his shaggy coat and went out to gather in my company.

IN THE city of Bordeaux at the Place des Quinconces,
where many narrow, winding streets converge on
the waterfront, stands a huge statue of Michel de
Montaigne, that great philosopher of Spanish-Jewish
ancestry, a bold rebel against unjust taxation and
mayor of that fair city of France.

The first faint streaks of dawn were showing in
the eastern sky on a July morning in the year 1777,
as two young men, so similar to each other in physi-
cal appearance and spirited manner that a stranger
would be pardoned for mistaking them for brothers,
met in front of the great statue.

The young man coming from the Rue Sainte Cath-
erine halted first, made a courtly bow, and smilingly
remarked, as he offered his hand, "We are the first
to arrive, *mon ami.*"

" 'Tis early yet, Marquis," replied the other, who

had arrived by way of the Rue Judaique (street of the Jews), "and we are so impatient to get away. Ah! Here they come now."

As he spoke, two men appeared from the shadowy gloom of the surrounding plane trees.

"Our good friends, Count Pulaski and Monsieur Kosminski, a young revolutionary patriot from Poland," said Marquis Lafayette, impulsively giving a hand to each and introducing his friend as Benjamin Nones, the son of the famous wine merchant.

Amid the general greetings a short, stocky, middle-aged man called across the street, *"Voila!"*

"Hush, De Kalb! Not so loud," warned Lafayette, "or we will have the civic guard upon us."

Others had by this time arrived. The Marquis counted them. "Eleven good men and true," he said, *"très bien,* but where is our twelfth comrade?"

" 'Tis von Steuben," replied De Kalb. "He will not appear until the hour strikes. 'Twould be a mortal sin for that martinet of punctuality to appear a moment before the time set for meeting, as, likewise, a minute after."

In the general laughter which followed, the great bell of nearby St. Michel tolled the hour of four and from behind the statue stepped a stout, florid Prussian.

"Ah, Count von Steuben," smiled Lafayette, "you are as regular as one of King Louis' famous clocks."

King Frederick the Great's stern and silent veteran

brought his heels together with a click and, without a word, smartly saluted the little group.

"Come, gentlemen," said Lafayette, "my ship, the *Auvergne*, is moored at the Quai de la Douane ready to carry us to America, where Liberty struggles with Tyranny. There lies our field of honor. Let us tarry no longer. Come!"

To their surprise and chagrin, however, when they reached the wharf, Lafayette's ship was dimly seen slipping down the River Garonne, to the open sea.

As the amazed company turned to the Marquis for an explanation, there was a clang of steel. A company of halberdiers surrounded them and De Tourny, Commandant of the *Garde Civique*, with a chuckle of satisfaction, stepped forth.

"Ha! Ha!" His over-plump body shook like jelly. "Am I not astute? I gave orders in the Marquis' name for that vessel to sail for the Spanish port of San Sebastian. King Louis!—*vive le roi!*—has forbidden the departure of Lafayette; and Maurepas, the King's Minister, orders his arrest.

"With you other gentlemen-adventurers," continued the pompous little officer, "I am not concerned. Go, if you can find a way, and be slaughtered with the *canaille* across the seas who honor not the majesty of royal blood. Now, which of you is the Marquis? I know him only by hearsay."

The comrades remained silent, being unwilling to aid the garrulous official.

"Come, come," blustered De Tourny, his face flushing with annoyance. "Are you he?" he asked, placing his hand on the arm of the tall, martial figure of Benjamin Nones, whose face he could not see in the shadows of the dawn.

"Lead on, good De Tourny," replied Nones facetiously. With a warning touch of his hand he whispered to Lafayette: "To the wine-cellars of my father at the quays. I will join you later."

De Tourny's stupid-looking soldiery led the prisoner along the row of quays, where the great arched vaults of the wine-cellars—Bordeaux's chief industry—loomed tomb-like in the gloom. Picking their way between scattered wine barrels and crates of bottled liquors, with here and there a laborer in shirt-sleeves and leather apron preparing a cargo for the morning tide, De Tourny could not resist the temptation to stop and boast to one of the sleepy harbor gendarmes of his important commission to arrest the well-known Marquis Lafayette. Thus, in the dim light of the early dawn, the party became scattered.

A sharp call from one of his soldiers made De Tourny turn.

"The Marquis! The prisoner!" the man cried. "He has gone! He was here a moment ago and then, *poof!* He disappeared."

De Tourny's legs quaked; the perspiration stood out in beads on his bald head. "Here, fellow," he cried to the nearest laborer, who, in shirt-sleeves and apron, was carefully checking a list of barrels. "Give me a taste of Medoc claret. I am faint."

The man tapped one of the smaller casks, and, drawing a taster's mug from his apron pocket, he gave the fuming officer a drink.

"Ah-h! That's good!" remarked De Tourny, smacking his lips. "But, the prisoner?"

The man shrugged his shoulders and, without a word, turned to checking his list again.

"*Mon Dieu!*" cried the frantic De Tourny, wringing his hands, as his men returned from fruitlessly poking their halberds between the barrels and hogsheads. "What shall I do? What will Maurepas say; what will the King think? *Sacrebleu!* Back to the inn!" he ordered, "maybe the cursed Marquis will return to his rooms."

As De Tourny hurried away, the laborer gradually worked his way along the line of quays, ever checking his accounts. Finally, after a cautious glance around, he entered one of the vaults and tapped at the latticed window of a little office-building within the giant arch.

The door opened and De Kalb looked cautiously out.

" 'Tis I—Benjamin Nones," the newcomer said. Slipping off the apron, he entered. "Are we all here?" he asked.

"Yes, Lafayette the Second," replied the Marquis, kissing him on the cheek in welcome and laughing

"See if you can fall back with your company by way of Sanders' Creek to Pine Tree Hill and save yourselves."

Major Nones, stooping to fill gunny-sacks with earth and stones, aiding his men to form a barrier against the next attack, straightened himself and saluted. His face was black with powder and dirt; a splinter of rock had pierced his forehead, and his sword, broken at the hilt, hung from his wrist. But his eyes glinted with determination.

"And you, Baron," he questioned, "do you stay?"

"Yes; I'll order no surrender; but save yourselves!"

"The covenant; remember the covenant!" Major Nones hoarsely whispered. "In the hour of trial and danger we— Ah! Here they come!"

It was every man for himself now. Redcoat, Hessian, patriot, mingling in personal strife.

De Kalb, white-faced and racked with pain from wounds, propped up against the body of his dead steed and protected by a little company of Jews, beckoned to Major Nones, who stooped to catch the whisper, "Retreat and save your men."

Too late! De Kalb had lost consciousness and Du Buysson, then the highest commanding officer, surrendered to the British in order to save useless slaughter.

Major Nones, Captain Jacob de la Motta, and Captain Jacob de Leon, of the Jewish company, then tenderly carried the brave De Kalb to the British camp; and as he passed from mortal conflict he gripped Benjamin Nones' hand and whispered, "Thank God our covenant remains unbroken."

o o o

The war was long since over. Benjamin Nones, now a partner with Haym Salomon, the broker, was sitting in the dingy office on Front Street, Philadelphia, meditating on the great events of the past. On the desk before him were letters from Lafayette and other old comrades, congratulating him on the marriage of his daughter, Miriam, to Joseph, the grandson of the highly respected and beloved Jewish merchant, whose financial aid to the Revolution had been as great as that of any patriot. As he sat there, the young people themselves entered, happy in the life-long pledge they had made with each other the day before.

Calling them over to him, and placing fatherly hands on their shoulders, Benjamin Nones again related the story of the covenant of his friend, the Marquis Lafayette, and that little band—a dozen heroes who came from overseas to help establish a nation built upon a covenant between men of all races and creeds.

"Be loyal to each other at all times," he said, with a vision, perhaps, of the thirteen weak colonies welded into one great republic—a republic that would covenant with all nations to bring about the brotherhood of man—the Republic of the World.

"When in 1781 the British Crown was dispossessed of its proudest appanage, the North American Colonies, there were many persons who eagerly called to mind the warning portent of 1761:

> " 'When first, portentious, it was known
>   Great George had jostled from his crown
>   The brightest jewel there,
>   The omen-mongers one and all
>   Foretold some mischief must befall,
>   Some loss beyond compare.' "

Extract from—

HUGHES and WRIGHT histories of England.

MOSES BENJAMIN FRANKS, a man in his early forties, short in stature, but broad-shouldered, sturdy, and mentally vigorous, stood on the portico of his beautiful mansion, yawning sleepily and gazing somewhat morosely at the river swirling past the grassy slopes of his extensive grounds.

His house was one of the finest in the ancient English village of Twickenham; and the stream was the River Thames, now half-hidden by the white, curling mists of an October morn in the year 1761.

Mr. Franks wearily passed his hand across his brow and then, with an impatient toss of his head, shook back a mass of dark, curly hair from his forehead. The famous banker, broker, and King's agent for the North American Colonies, was suffering from an unusual weariness, the after-effects of a gay "coronation" ball. Held in the grand salon of his home, the ball had lasted until an early hour that morning and was one of the many celebrations being held throughout Britain's domains in honor of the newly-crowned monarch—King George III.

"Confound these young people!" he muttered, half jokingly, half in earnest, "they *will* insist on making their parties gay and noisy, with new-fangled dances and novelties, mixing their drinks and their cookies and their confections, and what not. Then they drag us older people in, and 'tis we who pay the next morning! Ah-umph!" he grunted.

Mr. Franks hastily surveyed the surrounding landscape, a countryside of beautiful rolling hills dotted with the fine country homes of England's aristocracy. The entire panorama merged finally into the misty outlines of the city of London, some ten miles away.

The sharp, crisp air, laden with the faint odor of dead leaves and the aromatic perfume of chrysanthemums, stirred his senses into action. His eyes opened wider; he took a deep breath. "I'll go for a brisk walk, while the young sleepy-heads snore their brains away," he muttered facetiously. "It will give me a rare appetite."

Mr. Franks had strolled but a few yards down the circling carriage drive, however, when he heard the crunch of carriage wheels on the gravel ahead of him, behind the massed evergreens that hid the red-tiled mansion from the road. A light carriage had turned in at the great iron gate.

Somewhat surprised at so early a visitor, for the golden rays of the rising sun had barely tipped the tallest of the cedars that hedged his country estate, Mr. Franks cut across the dewy lawn in order to welcome the visitor at the threshold of his home.

A few moments later from around the bend in the road came a small postchaise.

"Umph! A Government courier, eh!" One of Moses Franks' odd idiosyncrasies was that of carrying on a running thread of muttered words.

The swaying coach pulled up at the broad steps; a lackey in plum-colored silk stumbled out from the rear and held the front door of the chaise open, revealing a sober-looking gentleman in a black suit. A third member of the company was a sergeant-at-arms in royal scarlet and gold, who stood stiffly at attention while the elderly visitor stepped out, wincing with pain as his foot touched the ground.

" 'Tis my gout, sir," he bleated. "And the celebrations of the past few days have not improved it, either," he added sourly. "These early morning vapours—" The man was evidently a chronic grumbler.

"You are, indeed, out early, sir," said Moses Franks, cheerily, his voice ringing clear in the crisp air. "But you are very welcome, sir, very!"

The visitor merely grunted as he slowly followed his host into the house, while servants who had hurriedly appeared took charge of the courier's equipage.

"I trust you carry no bad news, sir," said Moses as he swung the most comfortable armchair in his cozy library toward the cheerful little blaze in the open fireplace, and then rang the bell for coffee. "Your early visit alarms me."

The visitor, thawing somewhat under the warm and sincere welcome given him, shook his head. "Not bad news at all, sir," he replied. "But let me introduce myself. I am the Hon. Vernon Barclay, deputy marshal in the service of the Lord Chamberlain of the Royal Household, office of the Royal Jewels, at Westminster."

From a side pocket of his long black coat the deputy marshal drew out for a moment a small, white ivory rod, set with the royal arms.

Moses Franks nodded as he recognized the staff of office, then both men bowed to each other in the courtly and formal manner of the times.

"My instructions were to see you the first thing this

morning," the Government official continued. "The matter I have to impart is somewhat of a delicate nature, and my superiors thought you would prefer to do the business at your home rather than at your office in the city. That is why I came so early."

Moses nodded understandingly.

"Well, sir," continued the official, "you have no doubt read in the public press that as His Majesty left Westminster Abbey after his coronation yesterday, his coach was badly shaken while passing over the newly-cobbled roadway of Westminster Bridge. The finest jewel of his crown, a great diamond, was jarred from its setting and fell into the street.

"It rolled to the feet of an old crone who had forsaken her nearby den, where she earned a scant living by telling penny fortunes, to catch a glimpse of the grand coronation procession.

"One of the King's officers, Captain Bayswater, of the Guards, brushed her aside as he picked up the fallen jewel, saying as he did so: 'Begone, thou Witch of Endor!'

"The hag became furiously angry, for the crowd began to jeer at her.

"Waving her crutch at our smiling young ruler in his coach, the old Jewess cried, 'Beware, thou proud ruler! The richest jewel of thy realm may fall as easily as thy royal gem did slip from its fastenings on thy crown!' "

"Tut, tut!" exclaimed Moses. " 'Tis too bad that

such a thing should happen to mar so auspicious a day!"

"True," agreed the Lord Chamberlain's representative, producing a magnificent diamond from a silk-lined case, "but His Majesty, speaking between ourselves with all due loyalty and respect, is, if I may say so, peculiarly superstitious. Therefore, it is his wish, expressed through our office of the Government, that this jewel, which your honored father brought over from Hanover when he came with the late King, should be returned to you. It must never be used in His Majesty's service again."

An amused smile passed over the face of Mr. Franks. Lest his visitor should think him disrespectful of His Majesty, he strolled over to the deep-curtained windows apparently to examine the jewel.

Then he turned and spoke softly, "His Majesty's wish in this matter is a command, which I hasten to obey with all due respect. Please convey to him my loyal greetings. The jewel shall, in due time, be disposed of abroad and will trouble his Majesty no more. I promise you that!"

"Thank you," said the official, evidently greatly relieved. Then, growing confidential, he added, "Of course, as a trusted friend and of the same German nationality as our young King's late father, you not only know the strong points, but also the weaknesses of our new ruler, George III."

Moses Franks nodded gravely. "Yes, indeed I do.

He was a queer, moody boy, who built up idle fears out of morbid fancies, similar to this trifling incident of the Crown jewel. Forever brooding, no wonder his poor head aches! If such dangerous tendencies linger in his brain when affairs of state grow heavy, his mind may become clouded and ——"

"Such signs, alas, are already evident," the deputy marshal interrupted. "We must do all we can to check any superstitious ideas from becoming rooted in his mind."

Moses Franks nodded understandingly. "Aye, you're quite right, sir! I knew and understood his father, who was very friendly to our family in the old days of the Hanoverian Court, and I also know and understand his son. . . . God save the King!" he concluded gravely.

"God save the King!" repeated the official solemnly.

With this, the two men who sensed the tragic mental weakness of the young King long before the great majority of his loyal subjects, parted with a most friendly handshake.

For several minutes after his visitor's departure, Moses Franks stood by the tall French windows aimlessly rolling the beautiful crystal between his hands, while he watched the gardener and his assistant making their morning rounds.

Sounds of the awakening house did not disturb him—the bustling of servants, the turmoil of an awakening kitchen, or the merry laughter in the children's room at the top of the grand staircase. Moses heard them not. He was thinking of the young King. Would that weak mind stand the strain of Empire?

His half cynical thoughts were scattered as the door was thrown open and in rushed two children.

Moses turned sharply. Then his face became one broad welcoming smile as a dark-eyed, dark-haired, winsome little beauty, his daughter Rachel, ran toward him.

After her came the young rascal who had chased his pretty cousin down the stairs. He was called Davey but his full name was David Salisbury Franks. Long and lanky though he was, there was promise of great worth and character in the reckless, handsome face of the boy.

"What now, my little maid!" cried Moses, filling the room with the roar of his laughter.

"Oh, Papa!" The little girl exclaimed kicking her pantalooned legs in the air as, held at arm's length over her father's head, she caught sight of the flashing jewel on the broad window-sill. "Look at that pretty sparkling thing. May I have it, Papa dear; please?"

"Pooh!" said the boy. " 'Tis only a piece of shining glass. But, nowadays, girls want everything that tickles their fancy!" he added, mockingly.

"But may I have it, please?" begged Rachel.

"Darling," said her father, "this diamond belonged to our new King, but he doesn't want it any more."

"Why?" questioned the girl, opening her big eyes still wider.

"You are too young to understand, Rachel dear," said her father gravely, "and it's all nonsense, anyhow. But the diamond fell from his jeweled crown, and so he thinks it is unlucky."

"But why?" persisted Rachel, who had inherited the dogged, persistent nature of her father rather than the passive and contented nature of her mother. "Why?"

"Because everybody—except us three, of course," his eyes twinkled, "is silly and superstitious. Just because this crystal was jarred loose from its hastily prepared setting, people will believe that the King must lose the most precious of his colonies. Even now, the King's enemies are circulating their evil prophecies."

"Ha! ha!" laughed Davey. "Of course, sir, it's all nonsense, but why not send the diamond to the American Colonies? That might make the prophecy come true!"

Moses Franks, startled, looked piercingly at the laughing boy. Was the ever-recurring outcropping of radical and rebellious thought in this happy lad an inheritance from some ancestor of the past who, perhaps, had died protesting against the intolerance of an ancient regime? He wondered about it. The Franks family ever said of David Salisbury Franks that "he has always been a rebel, even from birth!"

"I don't believe such a pretty thing could do any harm, Papa." Rachel's puckered little face was comical in its solemn gravity.

"Then," said her father laughingly, "it shall be put in this great iron safe, by my desk here, to remain as a dowry for your wedding day." Gravely, the father kissed his little daughter.

"La!" exclaimed Rachel wonderingly.

> "Unlucky diamond! Bad luck 't will bring
>   To all who handle the baneful thing."

Davey's shrill voice rang out mockingly as he scurried into the garden.

"He's a witty young rascal," grunted Moses B. Franks, King's broker, banker, and purveyor to the royal armies in the American Colonies, as he called for his carriage and drove off to his London office.

❊   ❊   ❊

Twenty years passed. It was the Victory Year, and throughout the thirteen colonies the Yankees, as the British soldiery, now leaving this soil forever, called them, were celebrating the final victory, the surrender of Lord Cornwallis at Yorktown, and the birth of a new nation.

In the sunny parlor of David Franks' Philadelphia mansion that crisp October morning a notable group of Jewish people had gathered to celebrate the ending of strife. The Gratz, the Franks and the Hart families were well represented, along with several gentile friends of Haym Salomon and some others.

The gay company in the front room of the great brownstone house made merry over wine and nuts; and the younger element carried on their love-making in cozy nooks and corners, while the musically inclined gathered around the grand piano. Rachel Franks, now the loyal, loving, and patient wife of Haym Salomon, was upstairs in the children's playroom, cozily located under the broad eaves of the tiled roof, entertaining a group of young people, including her own little ones, Ezekiel and Sallie.

Rachel had been telling them of the King's great diamond and relating the many prophecies connected with its fall on Coronation Day, long before any of her young listeners were born.

"So now," she said, "I am beginning to believe that there may be something unlucky about that pretty bauble." Then a little undertone of fear crept into her voice. "It is indeed strange how misfortune does seem to shadow the footsteps of those who possess and handle great jewels, even as it did us."

"What happened, Mother?" demanded Ezekiel, her sturdy young son. "Maybe it's bogey talk, as you say, Mother dear; but tell us more. Even though it isn't all true, we want a story."

"Tell us the story, please!" The other children echoed his cry.

Rachel smiled at her impetuous boy. Then, with one arm behind his broad young shoulders, and the other around Sallie, she nodded pleasantly at the group of youngsters sitting around her feet, and warned them not to take too seriously the legend of the King's diamond.

"So you want to know what happened, Ezekiel," said Rachel, with a smile. "Well, the lovely diamond lay in my father's safe for many years. Meanwhile, war swept Europe, and over here a terrible strife occurred between the French and the British, a cruel, selfish, land-grabbing war, in which our poor settlers and pioneers, their wives and children, suffered most. And it now appears that neither England nor France will ever own any of our land, so that awful, savage French and Indian War was utterly useless and unnecessary.

"Meanwhile, my father, on one of his business trips to his various agents here, brought me with him.

"I made many friends among our people, both in Philadelphia and in New York, and as I did not like the sea and the rough journey across the ocean, my father left me in the care of Uncle Jacob, and returned to England.

"Then I met a wonderful young man, so loyal, so true, so brave, that although he never fired a gun or waved a bloody sword, he is today honored as one of our greatest patriots, our own, our very own Haym Salomon. Even though today he is broken in health and fortune, our little father remains calm and undismayed, happy to know that his great efforts helped to bring victory to our struggling patriots." For a moment Rachel's voice trembled and her dark eyes were dimmed with tears, but in a moment she smiled bravely and took up her story:

"When my father heard that I was to be married, he sent me the diamond that had remained so harmlessly in his safe year after year. It was his marriage dowry that had come to me as promised."

The spellbound youngsters clapped their hands gleefully.

"And who do you think brought it to me from across the ocean? Why, David, my cousin, who had grown to be a handsome fellow, ardent and of a very high spirit, but full of mischief and very fond of pleasure.

"He landed at Montreal, in Canada, where he was to be my father's agent. It was a bright May morning several years ago.

"The very next day the statue of King George in the main square of that city was found daubed over with paint and disrespectfully ornamented.

"David, seeing the crowd surrounding the statue, strolled up. He laughed aloud at the disloyal but witty inscriptions written upon it, whereupon a young French lawyer, by name of Francis Picote de Bellestre, upbraided him, and shouted that the perpetrator of such an outrage should be hanged.

" 'But, my good man,' expostulated David, sensing an opportunity for creating some fun and excitement.

Slipping a glass monocle into the corner of his eye, he drawled his words, aping the manner of an English court dandy, 'My good fellah, really! Don't you know, it's not the usual thing to hang people for such trifling things, even in deah old England! Eh, what?'

" 'Sacrebleu!—' The excitable Frenchman temporarily lost the power of speech.

" 'And really, now,' David was enjoying himself immensely—as he always did when a crowd was listening to him. 'It's not cricket, and what good would it do? A score of other saucy rogues would jump up with buckets full of red paint, and really, bah Jove, there wouldn't be enough statues of the— let's see, what do we call His Majesty? Ah, yes ——'

"The angry fellow lost his head entirely as he noticed the broad smiles around him. He suddenly slapped David's face and then pulled his nose, which, I must admit, was rather tempting, meanwhile pouring out a torrent of abuse in mixed French and English.

"My cousin suddenly became serious and knocked the man down. An incipient riot was only squelched by the timely arrival of the police. David was seized and rushed off to the town prison.

"The next day he was brought before the court. David fully expected to be lectured, warned, and then set free. But, much to his surprise, although his lawyer offered the extraordinarily large sum of fifty thousand dollars as bail for his future good behavior, he was denounced as a criminal and sentenced to prison for an indeterminate period.

"David demanded an explanation from his lawyer who called upon him in his cell. That gentleman explained that a very careful examination was being made of my cousin's bachelor apartments and of all his affairs.

" 'But it's all nonsense!' David raved. 'My kinsman, Moses B. Franks, is one of the best known and most highly esteemed men in the service of the British Government.'

" 'Yes, undoubtedly he is,' said the old lawyer, 'but you're not! You are too gay, too irresponsible, too fond of high life and low comedy,' he added dryly as he took a pinch of snuff. 'You'll have troubles galore unless you sober up and settle down.'

" 'When I get out,' snapped David, who was in a very bad humor, 'I'll see to it that—' He broke off as a sudden thought struck him. 'Why didn't those three old bumbleheads of judges accept that enormous bail you offered? That's what I want to know!' he cried.

"His elderly counsellor wagged his head. 'When a young man who has barely reached his majority utters disloyal expressions and is found to possess a diamond worthy of a King's ransom, the authorities become inquisitive. Probably that is why they refused even the high bail offered.'

" 'There!' exclaimed David, snapping his fingers, 'I fully intended to put that jewel in a bank vault for safety. It was sent over in my care by Mr. Moses Franks, of London, as the marriage dowry of his daughter, Rachel, who is to marry Mr. Haym Salomon, the well-known broker. I intend to take it to her personally at my earliest convenience.'

"My cousin was soon freed, but before he could leave for New York, the city of Montreal was invaded and seized by armed forces from the rebelling New England Colonies, led by General Benedict Arnold.

"After his release from prison, David was considered a sympathizer with the revolting elements of the American Colonies, a fact he made no pretense of denying. As such he was invited to the Victory and Liberty Ball given by the dashing and gallant young Arnold.

"Like attracts like, my dear children," said Rachel, "and young General Arnold's daring struggle through the dense forests of Maine and his dashing attack on Montreal, combined with his winning personality, found a counterpart in David. Instinctively, they were drawn to each other and their friendship was sealed by a wild, gay night, painting the old town red, as they say.

"General Arnold listened to David's 'Tale of the Bumbleheads,' as he termed his adventure with the three magistrates who had so hardly sat upon him.

" 'Well, then, Davey,' cried Arnold, 'I have good

news for you!' He slapped his thigh, making sword-straps and accoutrements jingle, and roared with laughter. 'I have a rich revenge for you. How would you like to escort your three bumbleheads into New England as prisoners of war? They have shown a disrespect to our great cause and to our worthy leader, General Washington, that warrants sending them, with others of like ilk, to Philadelphia, the very place you want to visit.'

" 'That suits my plans to the very letter,' cried David. 'I am with you heart and soul; I will enlist under you as a private soldier, if you will have me. How soon do you start?'

"Arnold laughed at my cousin's impetuousness. 'At once! We cannot hold Montreal, and must hurry away,' he said. 'But, first, a toast! Here's to our friendship, may it be ever victorious and prosperous!'

"Without any thought of what it might lead to, dazzled by the volatile gaiety of the brave young soldier he so much admired, David drank the toast, resolving to drop all other business in order to follow the fortunes of Benedict Arnold.

" 'And here's to your fair cousin!' Arnold raised his glass. 'Fortunate, indeed, is she to receive so fine a dowry as you have told me of.'

" 'I don't know,' said David with a frown, 'sometimes I think that diamond is ill-fated. I have fallen into more scrapes since I handled it than ever before in all my life.'

" 'Nonsense, Davey! Here, drink another toast, to General Washington and to Liberty!'

"And so toast followed toast, and David told me that at the end he did not have a very clear idea of what happened except that Arnold's forces had to scurry out of the city in great confusion and disorder. Grave trouble arose; there were charges of graft and corruption and a court-martial for General Arnold, from which he had difficulty in extricating himself because of his carelessness in financial matters.

"David stood by his friend during his time of trouble, overlooking Arnold's grave weaknesses of character and admiring his courage and ardent spirit.

"General Arnold was stationed in Philadelphia, and David, now a major and aide-de-camp under his command, was able to hand my dowry over to me. He left this city for West Point in company with his commander and friend.

"And then came the cruelest blow of all. The military idol of poor David's worship had feet of clay! Benedict Arnold had requested the command of the important military post of West Point to betray that fortress to the British. Had not the English officer to whom he had given the plans of the fort lost his way in the woods and been captured by American soldiers, the great treason might have been successful.

"When Benedict Arnold turned traitor, there was natural suspicion against everyone who had been associated with him. Although he was not implicated particularly, David asked the commander-in-chief for a court of inquiry so that his innocence might be proved. His request was granted and he proved his innocence completely. He was exonerated by the court, and retained his rank of colonel in the army.

"Although the defection of his hero and boon companion grieved him sorely, the incident sobered poor Davey more than anything else could have done. Losing none of his splendid qualities, David put aside that reckless, devil-may-care attitude that ruined poor Arnold. And David is still seeking for some sign of public confidence."

"But the diamond, Mother!" interrupted Sallie. "Why don't you wear the beautiful diamond and make all the other pretty ladies jealous of you? We haven't seen it for such a long time."

The elder children laughed aloud at the little girl's naïveté, but her mother smiled gravely. "I haven't got it, dear; so I cannot show it to you."

"Why? Where is it?" the children cried.

"The British in New York seized it when we fled to Philadelphia," said Rachel. "They robbed me of my dowry. Perhaps I shouldn't be sorry if ——"

"I wonder what King George will say when they show him the diamond," remarked Bennie Gratz, one of the older boys present; "perhaps he'll have one of his crazy fits again!"

Even Rachel joined in the merry round of laughter. In the midst of it there was a tap on the door.

One of the children opened the door. In walked a tall, well-built man, with bright, hazel eyes, a massive face, and a healthy, reddish complexion. He was clothed faultlessly, free and easy in his manner, and appeared as open and frank as his name might indicate. He was David Salisbury Franks.

"Davey!" Rachel exclaimed, springing to her feet.

The young man's face broke into smiles as the children gathered happily and proudly around him.

"Well, Rachel," he said brightly, his resonant voice full of his once gay laughter again, "everything has been straightened out. My honor is fully restored. Not only has Congress vindicated me, but it has given me four hundred acres of land. And that is not all. Here is a letter from Robert Morris, the financier of our Revolution, that I believe your dear husband, in his quiet way, got for me ——"

"What does it say, Davey?" asked Rachel. "Read it, please."

"It begins: 'The bearer of this letter, Colonel David Salisbury Franks, formerly an aide-de-camp to General Arnold, and honorably acquitted of all connection with him, after a full and impartial inquiry . . .' Then it goes on to say that I am to be sent by Congress to deliver a signed copy of the Treaty of Peace to our representatives in England for delivery to King George. I leave at once."

"Oh, Davey!" exclaimed Rachel. "There's that Franks' diamond again! They said it was a bad omen. Now you, another Franks, carry the fatal message that does really separate forever Britain's finest jewel from the Empire's crown!"

David nodded. "'Tis truly remarkable," he said with unusual gravity.

"I wonder what will become of the diamond, now that it is again in Europe," said Rachel reflectively.

"That reminds me," replied David, "Cousin Becky's husband, General Johnson, of the British Army, said that the British Government is selling the baneful jewel to the King of France just as quickly as it can. Why, Rachel! What is the matter? Why do you stare so into space? Speak!"

"I'm thinking, Davey!" Rachel's voice was low and quavering. Her eyes seemed to see something in the distant future that was terrible to behold. "If poor King Louis buys that diamond for Marie Antoinette, will it cause a French Revolution?"

David Salisbury Franks shrugged his shoulders. "Ah, 'tis all poppycock! Laugh, children, laugh!"

THE beauty of a tropical evening had come upon the little harbor of Fayal, in the Azores, as Uriah P. Levy, master and one-third owner of the schooner *George Washington* hurried down to the principal landing place of that Portuguese island colony.

To his surprise, the little vessel, which he had anchored only that morning near the British sloop-of-war *Vermyra*, had disappeared. Darkness now covered the town, but from the open doorway of a nearby inn hoarse sea-voices, roaring "Rule Britannia," indicated that the crew of the British warship was on shore-leave.

With a vague idea that perhaps some of the roistering sailors might be able to enlighten him, Captain Levy strode into the barroom. The sailors, stopping in their song, saw a young, cleancut, masterful-looking Jew of about twenty-one years of age, his sea-

254

bronzed face wrinkled in puzzlement at the turn of events which had deprived him of his ship.

"Hello, skipper!" roared a British boatswain. "So yer Yankee mate and crew deserted ye, did they? They took yer fine cargo of Teneriffe wines and twenty-five hundred Spanish dollars, too; so yer mate told one of our boys."

Uriah's face clouded; he clenched his fist. "I'll search the whole wide world for the traitors," he said, "and when I get them—" he stopped, at a loss for words to express his angry determination.

"And ye don't know the worst of it," muttered the boatswain, shaking his head and looking at the young Jew curiously. "When ye know all—" he stopped and took a deep draught from the pewter tankard before him. Then he continued, " 'Ere, skipper, drink to the King's navee!"

Uriah smiled and accepted the drink drawn for him. "Well, then, here's to merry England—may she stop seizing and impressing our Yankee sailors!"

The Englishman hesitated at this toast, and the boatswain spoke: "Matey, see here; speaking between friends, we sailormen don't hold wi' the press-gang, but the long war with 'Old Boney' has made it hard to get men for our service, and—" he shrugged his shoulders and hitched his belt. " 'Ere's to old England and George, 'er King!"

At the moment the tankards were raised, their foaming contents dripping on the sanded floor, the measured tread of disciplined men was heard outside. Then a British midshipman with six stalwart marines entered.

The sailors stiffened and briskly saluted.

"Is this the man?" piped the boyish voice of the young officer, pointing to Uriah.

"Aye, aye, sir!" replied the deep, booming voice of the bearded boatswain.

"To the *Vermyra* with him, then," the midshipman ordered.

To the indignant amazement of the young Jew, he was seized by the press-gang and hustled through the door of the inn and down the path to where the man-of-war's boat was gently rocking at the water's edge.

An hour later the warship had raised its anchor and was slipping out to sea under a favorable breeze and tide, and the young Jew was brought before Captain Scobel for examination.

"I will not take the oath, sir," said Uriah boldly, "for I am American born, and you cannot hold me; but until my release in an American port, I will serve in any capacity you wish."

"You show a better spirit than most of the scurvy rascals we have to impress for the King's service; but, like every sailor thus seized, you claim American birth. Where are your papers?"

"They are on my schooner, the *George Washington*, which has been stolen by my partner and mate,

Silas Boone, who left me stranded on that Portuguese island without money and without friends."

"Um! Well, we'll try you with the navigation officer. Go!"

Saluting the well-disposed captain, Uriah retired, to find among the coarse sailors a rough sympathy which made his disheartening position more bearable.

"Yer mate Silas was a dirty cur," growled the boatswain with an oath of disgust. "'E not only left ye marooned in that Heaven-forsaken 'ole, but 'e betrayed ye to our press-gang, and if ye ever meets 'im agin, plant yer fist square between 'is crooked eyes for 'onest Bill Marshall—that's me!"

With a smile, Uriah promised that he would do so.

Favorable winds continued to fill the enormous spread of the frigate's canvas and swiftly carried it across the Atlantic, to cast anchor at last in Chesapeake Bay where Uriah was able to present his demand for release to Admiral Cochrane.

The captain of the *Vermyra* reported that Uriah had proved himself a worthy seaman with a good knowledge of navigation and men of his training and ability were very scarce. Therefore, unless Uriah produced more direct evidence of his American birth, he should be kept in the King's service.

As the warship was to return to Europe immediately, this did not suit Uriah's plans, so one dark, stormy night he said good-bye to the *Vermyra* and its cruel discipline, its boastful, conceited officers and its alien flag.

Slipping down the anchor chains, Uriah sprang into a little boat tied to the stern of the warship and cutting loose rowed swiftly up the Potomac, assisted greatly by the incoming tide.

Within a few hours he again stood upon his native soil, the land he loved, America!

Losing not a moment, he hastened through the woods lining the river bank and soon reached a road.

A few explanations at a friendly farm-house produced the loan of a plump little pony, and within a few hours he was among friends in Washington.

A few days later Uriah received an invitation through his friend Captain Charles Stewart of the American Navy to attend one of the famous receptions given by Dolly Madison, the wife of the President of the United States, which was held in the grand drawing room of the White House, recently refurnished after the eight years of the presidency of Jefferson, who cared little for social affairs.

The First Lady of the Land was most gracious to Captain Stewart and his friend, Uriah, as was also the little, round-shouldered President. But just as President Madison was greeting them with quiet courtesy, there came a sudden interruption.

A coach had been driven up to the porticoed steps of the White House so furiously that several of the gentlemen present had hurried out in alarm.

The coach door opened and Robert Smith, Secretary of War, and Commodore Rodgers of the Navy stepped out.

"Is President Madison within?" the Secretary asked. His tone was very serious, his face pale.

"Yes," several answered. "What is wrong?"

"Gentlemen, we are now at war with England," replied Robert Smith gravely as he entered the house.

President Madison led the little group of men, including Captain Stewart and, by invitation, Uriah, into a small ante-room.

"Our ships must put to sea at once," Commodore Rodgers was saying, "and we need every seaman we can gather from the merchant marine service."

The President shook his head helplessly, for he was a studiously inclined idealist and not a man suited for war's stern duties.

A few days later Uriah P. Levy was appointed sailing master on the small, fine-lined, twenty-gun brig, *Argus*. Escaping the somewhat futile blockade of American ports which England had at once ordered, the swift little vessel was soon overhauling and destroying the enemy's merchantmen. When captured ships were valuable and swift enough to evade the English warships, they were sent to American ports under charge of prize-crews.

One morning the lookout of the *Argus* reported white sails on the horizon. Crowding on every bit of canvas, the brig bore down on the stranger.

To Uriah's delighted surprise, it was his stolen schooner, the *George Washington*, now the *King George*, with Silas Boone as captain and owner. The boat was heavily laden with rich Madeira wines.

"You double-dyed villain," said Captain Allen of the *Argus* to Silas Boone who had been transferred to the American warship, after Uriah had related his experiences. "I'd like to hang you from my yard-arm as a pirate.

"And I would like you to sail your recovered schooner back to America with a prize-crew on board, Levy," continued Captain Allen, "but I have sent so many of my men away that I would be sadly handicapped if an enemy warship appeared."

Uriah remained silent for a few minutes buried in thought and then he spoke, "If this man Boone and the crew he has misled will swear allegiance to our country and will help me sail the schooner to an American port, I am willing to forgive him."

"That's a generous offer," replied the Captain, "and I will give you one of my two 'Long Toms,' which will protect you somewhat should you be attacked. But you must be on guard again this man Boone's treachery. You shall take Jack Lang, of whose loyalty there can be no doubt, as your mate."

Thus it was settled. One of the two long cannons which peered out from the bridle-ports of the *Argus* was mounted in the center of the little schooner.

To make room for the cannon and its ammunition,

however, a portion of the rich wines from the schooner's hold was very freely distributed amongst the crew of the *Argus* by Captain Allen who, because of the great success they had met, felt kindly disposed toward his officers and crew.

Then late that afternoon Uriah parted company with the brig and steered the schooner's course toward the setting sun. From the *Argus* came sounds of hilarity, at which Uriah shook his head. " 'Tis unwise," he muttered to himself. "Eternal vigilance is our only safety."

His words proved prophetic, for the gray dawn of the next day revealed a brig of war, the *Pelican*, bearing the English standard of St. George, standing down under a cloud of canvas.

The little American brig with her lofty masts and long spars could easily have escaped from her heavier antagonist; but Captain Allen shortened sail and ran easily along on the starboard tack, while the *Pelican* came down on him with the wind.

At sunrise the drums rolled out their loud challenge on both ships as they beat the crews to their quarters. Then the *Argus* opened fire with her port guns, the enemy responding with her starboard battery and for nearly an hour the action was carried on with great spirit on both sides.

The American crew, however, befuddled with the choice liquors of the previous night, handled their guns badly, and as the two ships clashed for boarding, the decks of the American brig, raked by the enemy's guns, presented a sad scene, the dead and dying mingled with broken masts, cordage and overturned cannon.

Captain Allen and his chief officers had died heroic deaths; but led by midshipmen, the Americans prepared to repel boarders. Despair, however, settled upon them, for in the offing the British warship, *Alert*, was bearing down under full canvas to help her companion. Hope deserted them, and to avoid useless bloodshed, the *Argus* was surrendered.

The victors burnt the American brig to avoid its recapture, and then they sailed westward.

The next morning the *George Washington* was sighted. The *Pelican* bore down on her, firing a gun as warning to stop.

To the amazement of the British, the long gun on the schooner's deck was pivoted around and Uriah Levy and Jack Lang, with a cheer, fired a shot at the *Pelican's* tall masts.

Barely missing the mainmast, the shot wrecked the pilot-house. A second one ploughed its way across the British warship's deck, scattering dangerous splinters in every direction.

Then a strange thing happened. The British saw the crew of the little schooner throw themselves on the able gunner and his assistant bearing them to the deck, while the defiantly-waving Stars and Stripes at the masthead was hurriedly lowered.

Again Uriah had been betrayed by Silas Boone and his traitorous comrades, but the action had undoubtedly saved the schooner from being sunk by gunfire, for the enemy's guns were already trained upon the little vessel.

Uriah Levy and Jack Lang were hustled on board the warship and, with the other prisoners from the sunken *Argus*, placed in the dark hold, whose light came only from a single port-hole. Silas Boone and his mates were added to the British warship *Alert* whose crew was short-handed.

During the next few weeks many ships were stopped and examined by the two British warships. The *Alert*, being a much larger vessel than the *Pelican*, left her consort far behind.

Late one afternoon under gray skies and a heavy running sea, a large vessel was observed wallowing in the trough of the heaving waters.

Her badly-managed sails and poor seamanship convinced the captain of the *Alert* that she was a merchantman. His conjectures were apparently confirmed as he saw several men being sent aloft to shake out the reefs in an evident effort to escape.

The British warship bore down on her at top speed and fired a gun at which the larger vessel hove to and remained idly drifting with her untidy canvas flapping in the breeze.

The *Alert* passed by the merchantman's stern and when she reached the vessel's lee quarter poured in

263

a mercilessly cruel and unexpected broadside of grape and canister. The British cheer, however, was half-hearted, for even the rough sailors liked not the cruelty of firing on an unresisting, helpless vessel which had shown no flag.

Silas Boone with his little group of followers, taken into the British service, stood at their appointed quarters. They stared in surprise at the unusual procedure of a warship firing on an unresisting merchantman.

Then a little spot of color appeared at the mainmast.

"Look; 'tis our gridiron flag!" one of Silas Boone's men restlessly muttered. "This will be murder; curse 'em!"

Silas Boone's face flushed darkly and he, too, cursed under his breath. Then, as though making a sudden resolution, he gave one hurried glance around and, unnoticed, slipped below decks.

A moment later he was in the hold explaining the situation to the wondering prisoners. "We have treated you badly, Levy," he said, "but now, acting all together we may be able to seize this cruel Britisher and prevent the murder of our kith and kin on the high seas."

The little group hurried on deck. The guns had been reloaded and waited but the word of command to rake again the big, helpless vessel.

Then something happened! The disguised Ameri-

264

Down came a horde of Americans.

can frigate *Essex* being now alongside the *Alert*, without even waiting to open her ports, let loose such a tornado of point-blank gun-fire that the masts of the British warship splintered like matchwood, the decks were ripped up in every direction, while ropes, cordage and spars fell from aloft in a shower of debris and wreckage. Several shots passed between wind and water, and the sea poured into the hold of the *Alert* like a mill-race.

The smooth discipline of a British warship gave place to the moans and shrieks of the wounded and dying.

The little group of released prisoners suddenly produced from the recess of their clothes their beloved flag, and, led by Uriah, were cheering and waving frantically at the seemingly deserted frigate.

"There's our flag! Cheer, boys, cheer!" shouted Silas Boone. He was a traitor no longer, for he stood boldly on the ship's rail, holding on to the ratlines, pointing and shouting lustily at Old Glory.

Then a British sharpshooter in the fighting top of the tottering mainmast of the *Alert* picked him off with his musket and Silas fell back into the arms of Levy, his one-time partner.

His life was ebbing fast. "Tell our other partner, Thomas Jefferson, that I died—" he gasped, choked, and finally whispered: "loyal to you all!"

"If a man defeats his enemy, it is good; but if he wins the friendship of his enemy, that is, by far, a greater victory," Uriah said softly as he gently lowered his late partner's body to the deck.

At that moment the ships clashed and down from the overhanging frigate came a horde of cheering, determined, and raging Americans waving pikes, cutlasses and axes. Soon the fight was over. Captain David Porter, of the *Essex*, came on board and congratulated the released Americans on their escape from captivity.

Three weeks later, with ten prizes, including the *George Washington*, the *Essex* returned to New York to receive a never-to-be-forgotten welcome from the frenzied people of America.

Captain Charles Stewart met Uriah when he landed and hurried him to Philadelphia. There he pointed out a great new frigate of seventy-four guns, the finest in any navy, and the first of the new American Navy that was to arise on broad white wings to sail the seven seas.

"There! That's my new ship, the *Franklin*," Captain Stewart said, clapping the delighted young Jew on the back, "and I have a lieutenant's commission in my pocket made out for you, my lion-hearted Levy. Come, let's go aboard our new ship."

And thus Lieutenant Uriah Phillips Levy began his glorious career in the United States Navy that ultimately led him to the supreme command of the Mediterranean Squadron as Commodore of the Fleet.

LEVI MYERS HARBY, better known as "Captain
Charley," stood by the rail of Savannah's water-front
esplanade and watched with deepest interest the
maneuvers of Francis Fickett's paddle-wheel steamship, the *Savannah*, attempting to reach its midstream anchorage.

"Dirty, ugly-looking, floating pot-boiler," growled
the Captain, his jolly face clouding with disapproval.
"May they never take the place of our flying, white-
winged clippers. Bah!"

Then his face beamed with pleasure, for he saw
approaching him a portly, elderly gentleman of his
own people, whose every step showed conscious
pride. It was Judge De Lyon, a direct descendant
of that Abraham De Lyon who, with two score other
Jews, had come to Oglethorpe's settlement in Georgia
one hundred years before.

Captain Harby's attention, however, was attracted to the young girl by Judge De Lyon's side, his motherless daughter, Rebecca.

Surrounded by wealth and shielded by parental love from everything harmful, seventeen-year-old Rebecca De Lyon, in that beautiful climate, had developed beyond her years. The peach-bloom complexion of the South, enhanced by dark eyes joyous with the sparkle of mischievous youth and half-hidden in long silken eyelashes, presented a picture of budding womanhood.

So thought the Captain as he glanced from the tip of her broad-rimmed, brown straw hat with its crimson poppies nodding against her dark curls, down to her little silver-buckled shoes.

The Captain's heart beat rapidly as this vision of girlish beauty, smiling sweetly, ran impetuously to him and seized his arm.

"Captain Charley," her silver voice rippled, "where have you been?"

"I'm in disgrace," he said ruefully.

"Disgrace!" echoed Rebecca, her beautiful eyes opening wide in astonishment. "You, Captain Harby?"

"Aye! Dismissed from the navy; my ship, the *Beagle*, taken from me, and my commission cancelled."

"But why, my friend?" asked Judge De Lyon, puzzled.

"Well, Judge," the Captain replied, "after I left

269

Savannah last year on leave of absence I went west to the Mexican territory of Texas, where so many Americans have settled, and while there, I aided the revolt against Mexican tyranny, and so, for interfering in foreign affairs while in the U. S. service, I was cashiered."

Judge De Lyon clasped the Captain's hand in silent sympathy, while Rebecca's flashing eye and tapping foot betokened her impatience at the slight put upon her hero.

"We came down to the river-front," remarked the Judge, changing the subject, "to welcome a young man from England, one of our people, Aaron Wolf by name. He has come on that steamship that has just anchored. He is the son of an old friend of mine, and I have promised him a position in my law office. Let us go and meet him."

At the landing steps stood a young, pale-faced Jew, his baggage at his feet, while under one arm he hugged a tin box; in his other hand he held a violin case.

"Aaron Wolf?" inquired the Judge kindly.

The young man appeared relieved and prepared to make an Old World sweeping bow, but catching sight of Rebecca's bewitching eyes peeping at him from under nodding poppies, he lost his head completely and forgot the box under his arm as he sought to remove his hat.

The box fell, the lock broke and many tubes of

artists' paints were scattered over the cobbled esplanade. This increased his confusion so much that he blushed crimson and became speechless. Dressed entirely in somber black from his tall beaver hat, black gloves, cravat and high-buttoned shoes, he presented such a ludicrous picture that the irrepressible Rebecca was compelled to hide her merriment by looking at her pretty toes.

Suddenly the treacherous winds snatched the straw hat from off her lowered head, and a moment later Rebecca's cry, of astonishment more than of alarm, caused Captain Harby to look around from his self-imposed task of gathering up the scattered paints just in time to see the bowling hat spin over the seawall into the ruffled waters.

Then, to the amazement of them all, the long, lank, somber-dressed youth, clad in his best silk clothes, dived over the esplanade into the Savannah River.

A little crowd of wondering people hurried to the edge. Aaron Wolf was swimming gracefully back to the stone steps with the hat. A few minutes later with a bow that would have done credit to a Don of Spain, he had restored the dripping millinery to the prettily blushing girl, who, for the first time in her life, was at a loss for words.

Impulsively she gave him her warm little hand.

Her laughing eyes and sunny smile with the pressure of her dainty fingers thrilled him. From that moment Aaron Wolf worshiped her.

Judge De Lyon looked upon the youth with admiration. Such Old World gallantry was extremely rare, he thought, even in the South, famous for its courtesy.

"My daughter is wild," he remarked petulantly, shaking his head, "and will be, I'm afraid, until she settles down in marriage."

At these words Rebecca blushed furiously, Aaron's heart thumped with a wonderful new hope, while Captain Harby sighed as he thought of his forty-five years.

Without a word the little party entered the carriage Judge De Lyon had ordered, and as they rode through the city, Aaron's thoughts were as rosy as Captain Harby's were gloomy. On the outskirts they stopped at a palatial white house surrounded by dense shrubbery.

Entering the portico, they were met by Leonorean De Lyon, the Judge's youngest son, a happy youth of genial manners, who set Aaron at ease by laughing heartily at the story of the "run-away" hat, as he called it.

"Come with me," he said to Aaron, "I think one of my brother James' suits would fit you. He is away, in training at West Point." The young man led his new friend up the spacious stairway to his brother's room, and waited on the landing for Aaron to change his wet clothes.

Leaning over the balustrade, Leon, as he was

called, listened to the hum of conversation in the great parlor below.

A slow, peculiar drawl floated up, "—and the 'coon said, 'don't shoot, Davy, I'm coming down.'"

This was followed by general merriment, and Leon became impatient. He glanced inside the door.

"Come, Aaron. Don't fret over your limp cravat. Dave Crockett and Colonel James Bowie are downstairs. There must be news. Bring your fiddle, too; we love music."

Thus urged, and hearing Rebecca's silvery laugh from below, Aaron followed his friend downstairs.

"Now be serious and tell us your news, Davy," Captain Harby was saying as the young men entered the room.

David Crockett, a lean panther-like man in frayed buckskins, began to speak in a slow drawl:

"You all know how thousands of Americans have trekked to the Mexican province of Texas to cultivate the great plains and rolling prairies; you all know how riots and turmoil have overturned time after time the central government of that country, yet our settlers have kept the peace through them all.

"Then this Mexican dictator, Santa Anna, rises to power. He deprives us of self-government; he forbids the further settlement or trading of Americans in Texas; he imposes new and prohibitive taxes and persecutes us with military tyranny until we rebel.

" 'The gringos of the north must go,' he now says. General Cos, his brother-in-law, has been ordered to disarm us, leaving only one rifle to every five hundred inhabitants.

"Our people are rising. Sam Houston, who is staying on the ranch of Adolphus Sterne, one of your race, Judge, will lead us. Talk of secession from Mexico and a new republic is heard."

As he finished speaking, he sat down by the side of his friend, James Bowie, a light-complexioned man of about forty years, with a sad face, for his beautiful wife and their two young children had just died of the plague.

While his friend was speaking, Bowie's hand often wandered to the sheath by his side in which he carried the terrible knife made famous by his many adventures.

"My orders are to raise a force," Bowie said, "and try to hold back the Mexicans until Sam Houston's army is ready to take the field. I go to San Antonio; Davy goes with me."

"And I also," remarked Moses Levy, the leading physician of Savannah.

"That is well," replied Colonel Bowie. "The services of medical men will be badly needed."

"Let us have some music," said Judge De Lyon at this moment, turning to Aaron and introducing him to the little company.

Rebecca clapped her hands and smiled so sweetly

at the young man that his hands trembled as he played.

Love being in his soul, the listeners were somewhat saddened by the strange pathos that came from the instrument. Captain Harby, noticing the moist eyes of Colonel Bowie as the melody revived sad memories, said brightly, "Now, Aaron, let us have something stirring for the grim work before us."

Aaron, with a sudden swirl of his bow, swept into the stirring strains of *La Marseillaise.* As the last note faded away, Captain Levi Myers Harby strode into the center of the room and in a voice that made the dangling chandelier overhead rattle, cried, "By Heaven's will, gentlemen, we must have a revolution and a republic under the Lone Star flag."

Every man, Jew and gentile, present jumped to his feet. Colonel Bowie stepped over and wrung Captain Charley's hand in silent determination.

"Three cheers for the Lone Star Republic!" cried the irrepressible Rebecca looking at Captain Charley, her hero, through shining eyes of admiration. Her brother took up the cry, which was echoed by all present.

All was excitement in the little town of Savannah. Because of the stirring news from Texas brought by every incoming vessel, stern-faced adventurers prepared to "trek southwesterly by the lone star" to avenge Mexican brutality on helpless settlers.

Aaron Wolf, a newcomer to the New World of

which he knew little, had but one thought—Rebecca De Lyon. Late one evening as he wandered aimlessly through the spacious, sweet-scented shrubbery of the garden surrounding the great house, Aaron found himself looking up at the dark window of Rebecca's room, his yearning soul full of inexpressible longing.

Then his heart leaped within him for her window suddenly opened, he dimly saw her curly head and heard her soft call.

For a moment he thought she had seen him, and his joy was intense. Black despair gripped him, however, as a gardener's ladder was raised from below by someone until it reached her window. A moment later Rebecca, with a small traveling bag, quickly stepped down the ladder.

Aaron, unseen in the dense greenery, stood rooted to the spot in amazement. Then he heard voices.

Captain Harby was speaking very earnestly, "But perhaps your father knows best. 'Tis true, as he says, I am too old for you, and this young Aaron is gentle and cultured and is devoted to you. Your father's desire that you seek his companionship with a view to ——"

"But I could never love him," Rebecca cried petulantly, "I love you!"

"I was wrong to speak of love to you last year," the Captain murmured. "I will go away again and ——"

"Then take me with you; take me now, at once!"
She was clinging tightly to his arm.

"But—" began the Captain falteringly.

"I love you so, and we can never be happy apart."
Then came the sound of Rebecca's soft kiss.

The golden castles of Aaron's fancy fell into ruins.

His beloved's kiss also swept away the Captain's
self-control.

"Then come, dear heart," Captain Harby whispered passionately. "We will take the early morning
packet and slip down the coast to St. Mary's. There
we can be married, and I will leave you with friends
while I cast my lot with the Texans for liberty. When
I return we will seek your father's forgiveness."

As Aaron heard the soft steps of the lovers passing
on the gravel walk nearby, the veins of his forehead
stood out in agony, while his heart felt like lead.
Life in the new land now held no attraction for him.

He paced fiercely up and down, struggling with
the almost overwhelming desire to call the Judge
and stop the elopement of Rebecca with Captain
Harby, but when he thought of the Captain's kindliness to him, a stranger, he hesitated.

Looking up, as though seeking guidance from
Heaven, he noticed a tiny Texan flag placed on a little
summer-house by the enthusiastic Rebecca. The lone
white star on its blue ground reminded him of the
emblem of his race, the star of Hope.

Then he made a sudden resolution: he would go

with Colonel Bowie and the others and help defend this land against tyranny. Perhaps in death he would find the happiness that life refused to give. This thought revived him somewhat and he re-entered the house, to brood in troubled misery, however, until sunrise brought him better control of his feelings.

Judge De Lyon looked sadly at him as he entered the breakfast room, and replied to his greetings by quietly saying that his daughter would not be down to breakfast.

Aaron was surprised at the Judge's firm voice. Later in the morning, however, the Judge handed him Rebecca's farewell note, in which she asked forgiveness.

Judge De Lyon's face was aged and stern; Aaron's, stony with grief as they clasped hands in silent and mutual sympathy.

"She will be very happy with the brave and good Captain," murmured Aaron in a broken voice, "and we must forgive."

"Aaron, my son, you shall take her vacant place in my home ——"

"Sir! I leave tomorrow with Colonel Bowie for San Antonio; Dr. Moses Levy has accepted me as an assistant."

"God of Israel bless you, my son!" answered the Judge chokingly. "You are a credit to our people."

The next day the bugles sounded in Savannah's main street and under Colonel Bowie's command, the little band of heroes who were to strike the first blow that added Texas to the United States, rode away.

Day followed day, and soon the little company of four hundred Americans reached the outskirts of San Antonio, where General Cos, with fourteen hundred Mexicans and much artillery, was entrenched in the Alamo, a combination of fort and church.

Led by the indomitable Bowie and the heroic Crockett, men whose names alone bred courage, the little company stormed the Alamo, and the captured Mexican general with his soldiers were sent away under guard. Dr. Moses Levy went with them to tend the many wounded prisoners. Aaron remained behind.

Like some savage wounded beast, Santa Anna, "the Napoleon of the West," as he called himself, with his pride stung by the defeat, suddenly appeared before the battered Alamo with five thousand men, the flower of the Mexican army, and began a siege that has had no rival in history.

For nearly two weeks the Mexican artillery pounded the Alamo with shot and shell, while their infantry, raking it with rifle fire, charged again and again. Still the Lone Star flag waved defiantly in the breeze, as one hundred and eighty-three heroes stood their ground.

At daybreak on the morning of March the sixth, 1836, the little group of powder-grimed, bandaged heroes within the battered adobe walls of the Alamo heard in the distance the shrill *deguello*, "no quarter," bugle calls of the Mexicans.

Immediately the defiant melody of *La Marseillaise*, sounding strangely appropriate even on a violin, rang out in reply. This was followed by America's defiant war songs, hoarsely roared by manly voices.

Then, as the long-drawn-out lines of little brown, Indian-like Mexicans in their dirty-white, slovenly uniforms, led by Spanish officers in blue and gold, advanced over the yellow sands of the alkali desert, the last American cheer went up from the Alamo's battered walls, for the powder kegs were empty; and now it was every man for himself to do and die for Texas.

On came the Mexican infantry, prodded to action by lively cavalry in their rear. Over the walls they came. From room to room the slaughter raged, until, climbing back from over their heaps of dead, the breathless Mexicans sullenly withdrew.

Death and Santa Anna ruled the Alamo; not one American remained alive.

Among the few trophies gathered in front of the cruel Santa Anna was a smashed violin that never would play again; a tiny Lone Star flag taken from the body of a young Jew, who smiled at approaching death, an officer reported; and a little hand-painted cameo portrait of a smiling young Jewess, on the back of which was written "Sweet Rebecca, the fairest flower of all the South!"

Suddenly Sam Houston's little army, swooping down from the north to the cry of "Remember the Alamo!" trapped the Dictator's forces in the bend of the river and "Captain Charley," Adolphus Sterne, Dr. Moses Levy and other Jews, with their gentile comrades-in-arms, avenged the death of Aaron Wolf and the Alamo heroes! Santa Anna himself was led captive to the tree under which the wounded Sam Houston lay. There he surrendered Texas to its new settlers.

The revolution was over. Texas was a republic in fact, as well as in name.

The cameo portrait was given Captain Harby by one of the Texans who had found it on the body of a dead Mexican.

As he read the words and gazed into the beautiful face of his young wife, painted by the skilled, artistic hand of one who had loved so hopelessly, Captain Charley wept so freely that even his comrades who knew and admired his courage were puzzled at his weakness; but when he told the story of Aaron Wolf, there was not a dry eye in the little company.

As CHARLES FRANCIS ADAMS, United States Minister to Great Britain, stopped before the English Foreign Office, dark and dismal as all London's official and government buildings are, he had a presentiment of defeat.

This may have been due to the oppressive gloom of London's fog-wreathed streets and leaden skies or to his remembrance that the past summer months of 1863 had seen the tide of civil war running so strongly against the Northern cause that all men believed the young American nation would split in twain, to remain forever divided.

The shrewd diplomat, however, hid his fears beneath a calm and dignified exterior as he entered the massive doorway of the government building and announced his mission.

The doorkeeper, a uniformed "commissionaire,"

saluted stiffly, and without speaking beckoned to a haughty, bewigged and powdered footman in royal purple who, in turn, passed the diplomat on to one of the busy under-secretaries.

This pale-faced, round-shouldered scribe motioned Minister Adams to the cushioned seat reserved for visitors, while he, a silent emblem of official efficiency, glided through a green-baize swinging door leading into the realms of the great men of State.

Within a few minutes the American Minister was face to face with England's Under-Secretary for Foreign Affairs, Sir Austin Henry Layard, a very young man, who by family influence had been maneuvered into the high office which was far beyond his years, ability or experience.

From behind a great flat-topped mahogany desk this typical representative of England's ruling caste gave the ambassador a cold, non-committal welcome:

"My chief, Earl Russell, the Minister for Foreign Affairs, is indisposed," he said. "However, I am at your service, Your Excellency." Then he waited, impatiently tapping the desk with a pencil. He had scant sympathy with upstart America.

The elderly diplomat's quick eyes saw and understood. He spoke softly, yet firmly:

"May I ask whether you received my letter of protest relating to the two armored warships recently launched at Liverpool and now ready for the rebel service? My letter also contained the proofs of their

Confederate ownership, copies of the contracts under which the shipbuilders were constructing them, showing payments made from the proceeds of cotton sold by Bullock, the agent of the Confederacy, all duly attested by competent witnesses."

The Englishman looked bored. "Yes," he said. "My chief placed the matter in the hands of the law officers of the Crown before he became indisposed. There the matter rests."

"But these warships," Adams spoke impatiently, "which are superior in tonnage, armament, and speed to any in America, are now ready to sail at a moment's notice for the West Indies where guns and ammunition have already been gathered to send them, as the *Alabama* was sent, to prey upon our shipping, to break our blockade of the Southern States and thus to bring about the recognition of the Confederacy by Great Britain."

"Well?" inquired Sir Layard, in an affected drawl.

"The situation is already extremely critical," snapped the American. "The world's peace is threatened, for, as you know, President Lincoln's message to Queen Victoria stated that 'we are prepared to fight the whole world rather than give up the Union.'"

The deeply solemn voice of the middle-aged diplomat impressed the young Englishman. The noble head of whitening hair and firm mouth of Minister Adams confirmed Abraham Lincoln's wisdom in appointing him to that high position.

"Mr. Adams," Sir Layard spoke more respectfully than he had previously, "I realize your responsible, even critical, position in this matter. I will at once send a messenger to the Crown's law office, if you will wait."

In response to a ring of the bell on his desk, a messenger appeared and speedily hastened away.

"England's honor is at stake if she does not maintain her neutrality in this dispute between North and South," remarked Adams quietly, after a long silence. He was seeking a weak spot behind the Englishman's mask of studied indifference.

Sir Layard's boyish face flushed. "Honor" was his family pride.

"I but quote the remark made last night in the House of Commons by Benjamin Disraeli," the American continued soothingly.

"He is a man of mystery, an Israelite, and not one of us," Sir Layard curtly replied.

"But the common people show great faith in him, do they not?"

As the Secretary shrugged his shoulders in a noncommittal way, his messenger returned, bringing with him a gentleman of the law who was followed by a meek, parrot-like clerk.

After general greetings, the lawyer, Kennet Skene, spoke. He was an exceedingly tall, thin man, with mutton-chop whiskers. The tightly drawn skin of his face appeared as dry as his own yellow parchments.

"Your Excellency must know," he began in a dry, nasal, legal tone, "that we, Her Majesty's Crown lawyers, having duly considered all the data presented to us in this matter, have decided that the demand of the American Minister should be complied with, and that an order should therefore be issued prohibiting the departure of these vessels until the charges presented by the American Minister have been judicially investigated."

"Good!" exclaimed Minister Adams, his face wreathed in smiles.

Skene raised a long, thin, claw-like hand.

"Wait, Your Excellency," he warned. "The Crown lawyers must, however, call your attention to the fact that the affidavits furnished by you are *ex parte*. Paulus will explain." He turned to his clerk who stood behind him respectfully silent.

In a hasty, gabbling manner, as though repeating a well-learned lesson, the clerk explained that Mr. Adams' witnesses had not been cross-examined. If Mr. Adams should fail to prove his charges, by evidence which would satisfy the judicial mind, and the warships be released, the damages caused by arresting them might be very heavy.

The clerk further explained that it was a settled rule of procedure in the courts in such cases to secure the payment of such damages beyond any peradventure.

Skene, the lawyer, then stated that the restraining

order would therefore be issued, but it would not be enforced against the vessels until these damages had been secured by a cash deposit.

"How much?" Minister Adams demanded bluntly, disgusted with these legal technicalities.

"One million pounds sterling," replied Skene without a moment's hesitation.

". . . in gold coin!" came an echo, the voice of Paulus, the clerk.

Skene nodded, with a slight smile of approval at Paulus. His clerk was so efficient.

"Without the restraining order, these rebel corsairs may sail at any moment," thundered Adams. He turned toward Sir Layard. The crafty smile flickering around the corners of the Englishman's mouth angered him.

"Let me have this decision in writing at your earliest convenience," Adams demanded, turning to the lawyer. His voice was clear and sharp.

Sir Layard's smile disappeared.

"It shall be given you in full," replied Skene.

"*In extenso,*" echoed the clerk.

"But why is gold demanded?" asked Adams after a moment's silence. "Is not the bond of my government satisfactory; is not the word of honor of its duly accredited Minister to England sufficient? But stop! *Qui s'excuse, s'accuse!*"

"He who excuses himself, accuses himself," murmured Paulus, the echo.

"If those two vessels sail, it will mean war." With this parting shot, bluntly put, Minister Adams turned and strode from the little group of Englishmen and the British Foreign Office.

As he was driven back to the American Embassy in Grosvenor Gardens, Minister Adams realized that he was face to face with a situation freighted with peril and one which involved the fate of his beloved country.

He thought of Lincoln, the tall, impressive, gaunt President with those deep, wonderful eyes and still more wonderful patience and silent strength. He remembered Lincoln's farewell to him when he left the city of Washington for London, "You alone will represent your country at London, and you will represent the whole of it there."

What faith Lincoln had shown in him; and he sighed as he realized that he had failed, failed to keep England neutral, for undoubtedly the Crown lawyers never for a moment supposed that, anticipating their proviso, he might have provided himself with funds sufficient to cover an exorbitant cash deposit of £1,000,000. They evidently had planned that the two warships should be allowed to escape through this expedient, and that without delay.

"Hostilities are inevitable," Adams muttered, as he sat silent and downcast at his own desk, "unless a miracle happens."

But the miracle happened—an historic fact!

There was a light tap on his office door, and one of his embassy clerks announced that a gentleman desired an interview with the Minister.

"His name?" Adams inquired.

"He declined to give it, saying that he preferred not to do so. He appears to be Jewish, sir, and is evidently a man of culture and standing."

"Well, then, bid him enter," the Minister replied.

Adams rose from his seat as the tall, well-dressed gentleman, elderly and erect, his trim, snow-white beard giving him a venerable appearance, entered the room. His smile was captivating and Adams instinctively smiled in return.

"Will you excuse my odd, perhaps seemingly rude, request that I withhold my name?"

"Certainly," replied Adams cordially. He had intuitively recognized a friendly, sympathetic spirit in his visitor, and placing a chair for the unknown distinguished looking figure, waited for him to speak.

"I have come to offer assistance, if I may, to the cause of humanity and liberty which you represent," said the Jew looking directly into the eyes of the Minister and speaking with tense, deep feeling and frank sympathy.

Adams shook his head sadly. "Alas, sir, you cannot do that, however much you may desire it." He sighed deeply and sank back into his chair, with face haggard and troubled.

" 'Tis too late; I fear the die is cast," the Minister

289

added, moodily. "War seems inevitable. As you doubt-less know, all London is aroused over the events of the past week, especially the deadly work of the rebel privateers, the *Alabama, Peterhoff, Alexandra, Georgiana,* and others. The city is in a ferment. The whole hive of Southern sympathizers are active. And if you knew the worst . . ." The Minister shook his head despondently.

"But I do know the worst," said the visitor quietly. "My friend, Earl Russell, the British Foreign Minister, has told me all, and you must know that, personally, he is favorably inclined toward your cause."

"I thought that, too; but why his diplomatic indis-position at this vital moment?"

"Diplomatic statecraft," replied the trim-bearded Jew. "The Earl must obey the mandates of his class, whatever his personal feelings may be." Then he con-tinued, "Now may I be favored with the opportunity of making the deposit of coin required by the order?"

"One million pounds in gold?" the Minister ex-claimed, astonishment on his face and in his voice.

"Yes, Your Excellency; that amount shall be de-livered to the vaults of the Bank of England tomor-row, if you so desire."

Minister Adams stared at his visitor incredulously. "One million pounds in gold," he murmured. How often had he hopelessly repeated that phrase to him-self during the past few hours; somehow it sounded less fantastic now.

For several tense minutes there was silence. The elderly Jew, with wonderful consideration for the Minister's scattered wits, quietly arose and from a nearby window watched the falling leaves of Grosvenor Gardens' plane trees as they fluttered to the ground in the October gusts.

The trained diplomat, eventually recovering his composure, scanned the strong lines of his visitor's face against the light of the window and noticed that it was bronzed as though with sea-air and travel, and in spite of age, was radiant with health.

"Surely, sir," Adams countered, skepticism giving way to amazed wonderment, "so great an offer in so important a matter carries with it the necessity of revealing your name, even if given in strictest confidence to me, the humble representative of America."

The visitor raised a protesting hand. "I cannot," he said, gently but firmly. "Now," he continued, "it has occurred to me that if the United States had that amount to its credit in London, some question of authority might arise, or you may otherwise be embarrassed in complying with the condition, especially as communication with your government will involve delay. The breakdown of the Atlantic cable, as you know, precludes prompt communication. Therefore, the best way to avoid all difficulty would be for me to deposit the gold, which I am quite prepared to do. All I assure you of is my ability to effect the matter."

"I gladly accept your offer on behalf of my government," replied Mr. Adams, "providing some method of securing its ultimate repayment to you is found."

The unknown, yet impressive visitor, waved his hand deprecatingly.

"It might be proper," he said, "that some obligation should be entered into showing that the American Government recognized the deposit was made on its account; beyond that, I leave the matter entirely in your hands, Mr. Adams."

"The existing premium on gold is now sixty per cent in the United States," replied the Minister. "I suggest that ten million dollars of our 'five-twenty' bonds be delivered to you as collateral security for your loan in gold."

The unknown financier readily consented, and it was also agreed that in order to prevent the disclosure of his name, the deposit should be made in coupon form and not in registered bonds, the coupons being payable to bearer.

"And now may I ask," inquired Mr. Adams, "why you, a stranger, should so freely and so strangely come to America's assistance at this moment of her peril and in so remarkable a manner?"

"It is not America's peril alone," remarked the Jew, sitting down and facing the Minister. "Behind all this intrigue is that dangerous dreamer, Napoleon III, that pigmy nephew of a giant uncle. All Louis Napoleon's crafty plans to remodel Europe under the guidance of a reactionary Pope; to involve England and America in a suicidal war, which would allow the establishment under Maximilian in Mexico, of a Catholic Empire created and maintained by French bayonets, must be brought to naught in the interests of humanity and the safety of our people."

The Jew's eyes sparkled and his earnestness thrilled the Minister.

"I, a wandering Jew of great wealth," the stranger continued with a whimsical smile and a softened voice, "am constantly at work in all parts of Europe to mitigate the persecution of my people, seeking ever to hasten the day of liberty and justice. The gates of America, the New World, must be left open. No tyranny or intolerance must exist there. The doctrine of Monroe, your late President, must ever be maintained."

Again the Jew's voice was insistent, pleading and earnest.

Adams nodded his approval. He was extremely impressed.

"The tide of reaction has risen high in Europe since Louis Napoleon reinstated the Pope at Rome, whence he had fled," continued the visitor. "Even now the sad case of Edgar Mortara, the Italian Jew, is attracting the attention of all Europe because of its injustice.

"Secretly baptized by his Catholic nurse, who told her father-confessor of the action, this young boy was claimed by the Inquisition and torn from the arms of his mother, who died of grief a few months later.

"In spite of the frantic appeals of the boy's father and the Jewish community of Bologna, even against official protest from several European governments, the Inquisition refused to restore the boy to his parents. . . . Prussia has now threatened to intervene; but we have averted the peril of war by persuading the Jewish family to withdraw its complaint.

"While, therefore, we have lost in this case, for the boy is now the ward of Pope Pius IX and is being educated for the Catholic priesthood, the struggle of our people for liberty still goes on, and the Jewry of England is willing to aid the Northern States in maintaining the unity of that home of religious liberty and in keeping the evils of the past from returning to American soil and arousing again medieval hatreds and intolerance."

Minister Adams seized his visitor's hand, and the two men looked into each other's eyes with mutual and complete understanding.

At this moment the door was suddenly opened and a man entered breezily and unannounced.

"Beg pardon, Excellency! Thought you were alone." The burly, red-haired Irishman, whose loud voice filled the room, turned to leave.

The Minister called him back. "Here, O'Connell! Have you any news?

"O'Connell is a confidential and a very special

agent of the United States Treasury," Mr. Adams explained to his Jewish friend who was sitting beside his desk. "He is one of the many who are sent by our various governmental departments to carry out operations of which I am supposed to know nothing!"

"D—— the departments!" shouted the Irishman explosively. "Everywhere I go I find their agents busy, bargaining and plotting one against the other and even with the agents of the Southern rebels. But I have good news for you, Mr. Adams. I have just returned from the Continent—from Frankfort. If we were alone . . ." He looked awkwardly at the visitor and his red face became purple with embarrassment at his own impetuosity.

The Jew smiled. "You have secured loans from the Jewish bankers of that city for substantial sums aggregating millions, have you not?" he said quietly.

"You're right, sir," O'Connell admitted with a smile of relief. "I'm sorry if . . ."

"Mr. O'Connell," gravely interposed the Minister, turning to his Jewish friend and speaking slowly, "has spent his own private fortune in the cause of liberty—and he is a fervent Catholic!"

The twinkle in the eyes of the Minister found its reflection in the eyes of the Jew.

With the quick intuition of the Irish, O'Connell replied, "If we three, Protestant, Jew and Catholic, will get together for the sake of America, we will lick those Southerners before next summer and will make America what we all want it to be—a united land of liberty for black and white, with tolerance for all human beings."

The three men shook hands.

Thus it came to pass that through the loyalty, wisdom and firmness of Minister Adams, with the assistance of the unknown Jewish humanitarian—Rothschild, Seligman, or whoever he may have been—the rulers of England were compelled to change their plans. The two warships became units of the British Navy. Moreover, the plans of Napoleon III were brought to naught as he, with Maximilian, his tool, fell into disgrace and were swept away by the coming of a sound and lasting republic in France, which forever removed the menace of Napoleon's great name and intriguing influence.

The noble-hearted Jew died at an advanced age, carrying with him into the beyond many withheld details of the powerful influence he had wielded in behalf of his people and for humanity.

In time to come, the certain identity and complete story of the quiet, elderly gentleman who is now known in history as "The Unknown Jew who saved the Union," may yet be revealed.

"ENGLAND is most certainly going to the dogs!"
growled Lord Randolph Churchill impatiently rising
from a comfortable lounge chair and selecting a decanter of port from a nearby rack of liqueurs.

The conversation in London's famous aristocratic
Carlton Club had turned upon the decay of the once
powerful Conservative Party of England since the
death of its great leader, Lord Beaconsfield, better
known as Benjamin Disraeli.

"Yes," replied Sir John Gorst, a mild mannered,
dignified gentleman, from the depths of a similar
lounge. "If only we could instill into the minds of
our people the spirit of Disraeli; imbue them with
pride in their imperial heritage as he did—" he
sighed and shook his head despondently.

The silence which followed was broken by a rubi-
cund-faced member stepping over to a nearby table,

on which stood a large china bowl of wild English primroses, freshly gathered—it was springtime in England. He twirled one of the daintily-fragrant pale yellow flowers in his fingers for a moment. Then he turned to the little group of gloomy-faced men and with the sunny smile of optimism said,

"Gentlemen of England—" and there spoke the diplomat, for an answering thrill ran through each man present; their faces grew expectant, for the famous raconteur, Sir Henry Drummond Wolff, was speaking. "Gentlemen of England," he said, "our Disraeli greatly loved this native flower which so profusely carpets our countryside each spring. We honor his memory by displaying this humble little blossom in these gorgeous rooms; why not found a Primrose League among our people, with dear old Dizzy's favorite flower as its emblem?"

Thus the Primrose League of the British Empire was born from the inspiring memory and love which the British people bore for Benjamin Disraeli, a Jew of Spanish descent. Within a few years over two million members wore the primrose badge on Primrose Day. Sir Henry Drummond Wolff, its Jewish founder, had risen from honor to honor, until at the beginning of our story we find him installed as England's Ambassador to the Spanish Court at Madrid.

It was the morning after the revelry of St. Valentine's Day, 1898. Donna Rebecca Sylvia, maid to the Queen-Mother, peeping through the half-open door of the apartment allotted to the British Ambassador on his visits to the royal palace, saw that gentleman sound asleep at his table, evidently overcome with the festivities of the previous night, in which he had played no slight part.

Stealthily stepping across the soft carpet, she reached the table. Glancing curiously at the little bouquet of English primroses on it she searched quickly through a pile of unopened correspondence neatly stacked by the side of the flower vase. Then with a sigh of satisfaction, she seized upon a yellow-enveloped telegram.

"This must be it," she whispered to herself. "He said it was in a yellow envelope."

Before she could flee, however, a young man in crimson and gold, the colors of royal Spain, boldly entered the room.

"Sylvia," he hoarsely whispered, "why are you stealing the Minister's correspondence?" His voice trembled with pain and anxiety. He saw the telegram in her hand.

The girl's pretty face flushed crimson but she tossed her shapely head of dark curls and daringly thrust the telegram into the bosom of her dress.

The youth's dark face crimsoned with anger as he stepped toward her, and she, stepping back against the table, aroused the Minister from his slumber.

The page, bowing low, murmured an apology for his intrusion.

Ignoring the boy, Minister Wolff smiled and bowed toward the girl, who returned his bow with as stately a curtsy as though she had been the Queen-Mother herself. The Minister looked inquiringly at the young girl of about twenty years of age, vivaciously beautiful with the soft, rich complexion that only generations of warm southern skies can give. Her eyes were dark, "a bewitching little maid of Jewish extraction," remarked the Minister to himself.

"What is your name, Senorita?" he inquired with a smile.

"Donna Rebecca Sylvia," she replied softly.

"de Machado," added the page sullenly. "She is my sister, a wilful and foolish girl. I came to this corrupt Court to watch over her safety, for I am David de Machado, the last of our house." The young man drew himself up proudly.

The Minister nodded understandingly. "Well?" he said.

David looked at his sister and both hesitated to speak. Then Sylvia drew from the bosom of her dress a primrose.

"I was curious, such a strange flower, we do not have its kind in Spain. What is it, Senor?"

"It is an English wildflower, the primrose, called in Spanish, *primavera*. It was the favorite flower of one of our own people, a great leader, Benjamin Disraeli."

"We are Jews also," said David de Machado proudly, "but I think my sister honors not our family name by coming to this decadent Court to receive favors from those who have persecuted our race."

"But we are Christians now," replied the girl, her hand instinctively straying to a tiny gold cross hanging by the daintiest of chains from her shapely neck.

"Dost remember the crucifixion of our ancestors?" Her brother spoke sharply. "Was not our ancestor, Isabel de Machado, a victim of the *auto da fé* in yon square now so gaily decorated for St. Valentine's feast?"

"That was long ago," replied the girl lightly, "and is forgotten by all save those who brood on such dismal things. The Queen-Mother, whom I serve, treats me kindly, as does all the Court, and the men are all so gallant and gay."

"Aye, there's reason for it," growled David. "That treacherous Canovas del Castillo, whose evil leadership curses our country, who suppresses our liberties, who sent General Weyler to become the 'Butcher of Cuba,' he ——"

"Treats me most kindly," interrupted his sister. "I will not hear a word said against him."

"You are his spy!" shouted David, losing all patience, forgetting everything in his anger. You have just stolen Senor Wolff's telegram at the command of this beast Canovas! *I* saw it in your hand, when I entered the room."

The Minister raised his hand. "Peace!" he ordered quietly and firmly. His astute diplomatic mind was working rapidly. He would take his time and by questioning this young girl, evidently a tool of wiser heads than hers, find out the truth.

But, as though to mock and upset his plan, an uproar arose from the street. From the windows could be seen great angry crowds sweeping from converging streets into the gaily-decorated square. The bright-colored flag of Spain fluttered in a thousand hands, the roaring mobs surged around the armed sentries and beat against the palace gates.

"I wonder what—?" the Minister began. Then, turning to the girl, he said, "Give me my telegram, quick!"

Unable to utter a word, and biting her lips in shame, Sylvia handed him the message she had been instructed by Canovas to procure.

It was in code, but the Minister read it at once.

He raised his eyebrows in surprise and muttered, " 'Tis the end of Spain's Western dominion." It told of the sinking of the United States cruiser, *Maine*, in the harbor of Havana, Cuba, the previous evening.

Then came the steady roar of the crowds outside: "Down with Canovas! Down with the traitor! *Viva España!*"

A hush suddenly fell upon the people. The folding French windows above the massive doors of the palace had opened and a stately woman stepped out into the sunshine and faced the excited people. Her hand was on the shoulder of a pale, slightly-built twelve-year-old boy. The crowds saw their young ruler, Alfonso XIII, and his mother, Queen Maria Christina.

The volatile people of Spain went from one extreme to the other, and in place of threatening curses and missiles there poured forth a swelling tide of patriotic cheering until a regiment of cavalry, their swords flashing in the sun, peacefully dispersed the mob.

Meanwhile within the palace all was excitement.

Dismissing the young people with a few kindly words, after securing their pledge of silence on the matter, Minister Wolff hurried to the Premier's apartment in response to a call from Canovas.

Sir Henry Drummond Wolff found that stern-faced man alone. He was sending messages and receiving telephone calls; between calls he strode up and down the room, savagely chewing at his white moustache.

As the Ambassador entered, however, Canovas, as a grandee of Spain, received him with extravagant politeness, offering him the choicest liqueurs and the finest cigars.

Minister Wolff took the proffered chair, but the Premier, too disturbed to sit, remained standing and calculatingly watched the Ambassador with piercing, steel-gray eyes.

"This is a sad happening, Your Excellency," the Premier said, "the destruction of the American warship, *Maine*, in Havana harbor last night."

"It is, indeed," agreed the Englishman, "and if the services of my ———"

Canovas waved his arm as though brushing aside the empty verbiage of diplomacy, and sharply interrupted, "War is inevitable. 'Tis useless to waste words. Those interfering Americans are wholly to blame for the catastrophe which has come upon them. When Weyler, our gallant general, sought to crush the Cuban rebellion, it was American sympathy and assistance which kept the Cubans arrayed against us."

The angry man strode up and down the room, then turned and faced the Minister. "America, too, gave refuge in her southern cities to those rebels who escaped from our prison camps. Now, by sending her warship, she has brought upon herself the judgment of God!"

Minister Wolff silently contemplated the ash of his cigar. After appraising the Ambassador with slightly puckered eyebrows, Canovas continued, almost persuasively, but with the direct driving force that was so characteristic of that great master-mind of Spain, "Senor, has not the time arrived to test that absurdity of an upstart nation—the Monroe Doctrine?

"The governments of Europe are with Spain in this crisis. His Majesty, the Kaiser, has this morning assured us personally that we have his good will. It remains only for England with her tremendous influence to act likewise, and these presumptuous Americans will find a world arrayed against them."

He stopped and waited for Minister Wolff to speak.

The Ambassador was thinking of one word, "PRIM-ROSE," the signature of that code telegram. To him that word was his answer. England and her great wide-flung empire were so closely allied by manners, customs, and language to the great English-speaking American nation that there could be but one reply.

"England's policy, if eventualities happen," replied Minister Wolff slowly, "will be strict neutrality. But if my humble services can aid in maintaining friendly relations between America and Spain, I beg of you ——"

"The fleets of Spain will depart under Admiral Cervera to maintain our honor in the West," interrupted Canovas bluntly.

"Well, *coal is contraband!*"

"*Sacra Maria!*" muttered the Premier angrily. His cup of bitterness overflowed. His last card had been played.

At this moment there was a sharp rap at the door. It was opened and a little group of palace guards with David de Machado in their midst entered the room. They silently saluted.

"What is the meaning of this, Captain Pavia?" demanded Canovas addressing the officer in charge.

"When we dispersed the rabble in the square, Senor," replied the officer, "we noticed this royal page encouraging them from a palace window. He was shouting, 'Down with Canovas! Kill the traitor!!'"

The Premier's face darkened. "So you would kill me, would you?" he thundered, facing the young Jew. "Then, if you are so anxious to kill, there is work for you to do in Cuba!"

"You oppressor of the people," cried the youth. His captors were cruelly twisting his arms backwards, while Canovas smiled sardonically. "May you die the death of a dog before ever I see Cuba!"

"Away with him!" ordered Canovas, his spirits somewhat restored by this incident. "And now, *buenos dias, Senor*," he said, turning to the Minister and bowing gracefully.

Then followed hectic days, days full of martial music, of parades and speeches, when latent dislike of the despised *Americanos* was fanned into passionate hatred. The war, now started, was carried on week after week with boastful pride and show, while promises of great victories on land and sea were read in the screaming newspaper headlines by the people.

Great was the activity behind the scenes. While America was mobilizing an army in record time, the secret diplomacy of European Courts was seeking to combine forces on behalf of bankrupt Spain.

Sylvia de Machado, dismissed from Court after the arrest of her brother, in her loneliness had sent the little primrose given to her by Minister Wolff to his embassy in the *Calle Fernando el Santo* with a note explaining her need of counsel.

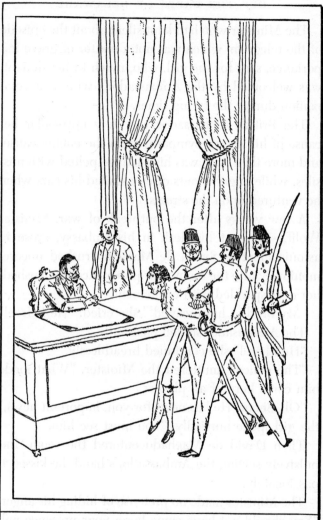

"You oppressor of the people."

The Minister who had kept silent about the episode of the telegram, which was not a matter of grave importance, sent for the girl, who, much to her delight, was welcomed by the Ambassador's wife as a companion during the trying times.

The British Ambassador was very unpopular because of his known sympathy with the enemy cause; and more than once was his carriage pelted with missiles, while angry shouts often assailed his ears when he ventured upon the streets.

A few weeks after the outbreak of war, Minister Wolff, sitting at his desk in his embassy, arose in astonishment as Sylvia de Machado rushed unceremoniously into the room. Her pretty face was flushed; her eyes sparkled with excitement.

"My brother has escaped!" she cried. "He is free!"

The Ambassador smiled pleasantly.

"He's here!" she continued breathlessly.

"The deuce!" muttered the Minister. "What made him come here of all places?"

"Oh, Senor! He has news for you, important news," the girl spoke hurriedly. "You must see him."

Then David de Machado entered the room. Impulsively seizing the Ambassador's hand, he kissed it passionately.

The Minister made no pretense of hiding his anger. "You should not have come here; your presence will only add to our troubles."

"Hear me, Senor, and you will forgive," David

begged. "Seeking revenge, I hastened to Canovas' house, and while hidden there, I overheard one of his dangerous plots of which you should be informed. So I saved my vengeance for a future day, and came here to warn you."

"What is this plot?" inquired the Minister briefly.

Then David described a carefully prepared plot of which the Ambassador knew nothing.

"My government should know of this immediately," muttered the Minister, pacing the floor excitedly. "But how? The telegraph is of no service; my messages are delayed or stopped, and a moment's delay may fail to prevent this further catastrophe."

It was David who spoke. "Your Excellency, may I take your message to England? The ponies are even now waiting to take me to the coast and the steamer will carry me quickly to England. The plans made to save me may also aid you, Senor."

Hope appeared in Ambassador Wolff's face, but he hesitated. "Can I trust you, David?" he asked.

The young man drew from his peasant's blouse a withered and broken primrose. "The Primrose League—of Israel," he spoke half-jestingly, half-earnestly, "Senor, I'll give my life for it, if needs be." His voice trembled with emotion. Tears filled Sylvia's eyes and a lump came into the Minister's throat.

"Well, then, go! But stay in London, David; we may all meet there before long."

So David went, and no word came from him. But

Minister Wolff heard a few days later that the German warship, *Irene,* in Manila Bay had placed herself between the guns of Admiral Dewey's fleet and the Spanish fortress in an antagonistic manner, and that swift British cruisers had come steaming into the harbor, dense clouds of smoke pouring from their funnels as though under forced draught. Minister Wolff chuckled for he knew that David had carried his message safely to London, and that the transfer of Philippine sovereignty to the restless Kaiser had been frustrated.

The Minister had other troubles, however, for Canovas was killed by the bullet of an unknown assassin. David, the escaped prisoner, whose threatening words were recalled, was suspected. Since Sylvia, his sister, was known to be attached to the household of the Ambassador, the strained relations became almost unbearable.

The Minister would not allow Sylvia to be removed from his protection, claiming that his embassy was inviolable under international law, and declaring also that he had evidence that David had left the country before the assassination of the Premier. Further than that he would give no information.

With the downfall of Canovas' rule of force, the small yet powerful Liberal Party of Spain came into office. Minister Wolff on his first visit to the new Premier, the benign Senor Sagasta, urged peace so strongly that the French Ambassador was sent for.

Soon the Western Empire of Spain became a dream of the past. Peace once again reigned between the nations, but not in Madrid! Thousands of employees of the great tobacco companies of the city, impoverished and ruined by the war, rioted for many days. During this period of turmoil, the British Ambassador with all his household left for home.

It was springtime again in England, and as the South Coast express train pulled into Charing Cross station in London, Ambassador Wolff stepped out of a first-class carriage, followed by his wife and Sylvia, who had become almost a daughter in his family. They were met by the cry of a street hawker, " 'Ere you are, sir, sweet English primroses, penny a bunch! Buy yer li-dies sweet English primroses!"

The Ambassador, his face beaming good-naturedly, gave the man a shilling and presented his lady companions with the fragrant bouquets.

Then David de Machado came hurrying down the platform. He delightedly greeted his sister with a kiss and bowed to his friends in that extravagant manner of Spain so out of place in the prosaic gloom of a London railway station.

"Your Excellency," said David, almost overcome with his emotions, "your influence with Commander Adolphus Marix, our co-religionist on the *Maine* inquiry board, has secured me an introduction to Havana's greatest firm of tobacco producers and exporters. My sister and I will leave for Cuba soon."

"And I am going to serve my country as Ambassador to Turkey," replied Minister Wolff. "First, however, you must come to the Carlton Club and tell your story. It will show our wine-bibbling pessimists that the spirit of Disraeli is still with us in the world today."

312

LIST OF REFERENCES

In collecting historical data for the foregoing stories, the following authorities were used very freely:

JEWISH

The voluminous *Publications* of the American Jewish Historical Society. (Indicated as A. J. H. S.)

The Jewish Encyclopedia.

HYAMSON, A. M., *Great Britain and the Jews.* The Edinborough Press, London. 1918.

KOHUT, G. A., *Sketches of Jewish Life in the South American Colonies.* The Levytype Co., Philadelphia. 1895.

MAGNUS, K., *Outlines of Jewish History.* The Jewish Publication Society of America, Philadelphia. 1890.

MARGOLIOUTH, M., *History of the Jews in Great Britain.* R. Bentley, London. 1851.

MARKENS, I., *The Hebrews in America.* Privately printed, New York. 1888.

PETERS, M. C., *Justice to the Jew.* T. F. Neely, New York. 1899.

WIERNIK, P., *History of the Jews in America.* Jewish Press Publishing Co., Philadelphia. 1931.

NON-JEWISH

Bureau of American Ethnology, Washington, D. C., *Handbook of the American Indians.* 1907-1910.

Encyclopædia Britannica.

FISHER, S. G., *Men, Women and Manners in Colonial Times.* J. B. Lippincott Co., Philadelphia. 1898.

LLORENTE, J. A., *History of the Spanish Inquisition*. G. C. Morgan, New York. 1826.

MACAULEY, T. B., *History of England*. Longmans, Green & Co., London. 1897.

National Encyclopedia of Reference. Standard Bookbinding Co., New York. 1912.

Nelson's Encyclopedia. T. Nelson & Sons, New York. 1906.

PRESCOTT, W. H., *History of the Reign of Philip the Second*. Phillips, Sampson & Co., Boston. 1858.

———, *History of the Reign of Ferdinand and Isabella*. American Stationers Co., Boston. 1838.

ROBERTS, G., *The Social Life of England in Past Centuries*. Longmans & Roberts, London. 1856.

SOUTHEY, R., *History of Brazil*. Longmans & Co., London. 1817.

SPARKS, J., *American Biography*. Harper & Brothers, New York. 1902.

———, *The Life of George Washington*. Tappan & Dennet, Boston. 1842.

OFF THE CAPES OF DELAWARE

FRIEDENWALD, H., "Jacob Isaacs and His Method of Converting Salt Water into Fresh Water," A. J. H. S. *Publications*, II, 111; also Vols. VIII, IX, and XXVI (notes).

JOHNSON, A., *The Swedish Settlements on the Delaware*. D. Appleton & Co., New York. 1911.

IN THE DAYS OF WITCHCRAFT

ADAMS, N., *Life of John Eliot*. Massachusetts Sabbath School Society, Boston. 1847.

BACON, O. N., *History of the Town of Natick*. Damrell & Moore, Boston. 1856.

CALEF, R., *More Wonders*. J. D. & T. C. Cushing, Salem, Mass. 1823.

FISHER, S. G., *Men, Women and Manners in Colonial Times*. (The nature and character of the Puritans, p. 167.) J. B. Lippincott Co., Philadelphia. 1898.

FRIEDMAN, L. M., "Early Jewish Residents in Massachusetts," A. J. H. S. *Publications*, Vol. XXIII.

————, "Cotton Mather and the Jews," A. J. H. S. *Publications*, Vol. XXVI.

Johnson's *Wonder-Working Providence in New England.* Charles Scribner's Sons, New York. 1910.

LEBOWICH, J., "The Jews in Boston," A. J. H. S. *Publications*, Vol. XII.

MATHER, C., *Magnalia Christi Americana* (ecclesiastical history of New England). T. Sowle, London. 1703.

————, *Memorable Providences* (relating to witchcraft and "possessions"). J. Brunning, Boston. 1689.

————, *The Wonders of the Invisible World.* J. Dunston, London. 1693.

MATHER, H. E., *The Lineage of Richard Mather.* Hartford, Conn. 1890.

"YE JEW DOCTOR OF MARYLAND"

ALTFELD, E. M., *The Jews' Struggle for Religious Liberty in Maryland.* M. Curlander, Baltimore. 1924.

BROWNE, W. H., *Maryland.* Houghton, Mifflin & Co., Boston. 1904.

"Excelsior" *History of the United States* (Roman Catholic edition). W. H. Sadlier, New York. 1905.

HALL, C. C., *Narratives of Early Maryland.* (Containing descriptive letter sent to Rome by Father Andrew White upon his arrival in Maryland, 1634.) Charles Scribner's Sons, New York. 1910.

HOLLANDER, J. H., "Some Unpublished Material Relating to Dr. Jacob Lumbrozo, of Maryland," A. J. H. S. *Publications*, Vol. I.

HÜHNER, L., "Jewish Women in America." Pamphlet, reprinted from *The American Hebrew* magazine. 1918.

Jewish Encyclopedia. Article "Lumbrozo, Jacob."

SCHARF, J. T., *History of Maryland.* (The arrival of the *Ark* and the *Dove* at Maryland.) J. B. Piet, Baltimore. 1897.

SILBER, M., *Jewish Achievements*. Modern View Publishing Co., St. Louis. 1910.

WIERNIK, P., *History of the Jews in America*. Jewish Press Publishing Co., Philadelphia. 1931.

THE MYSTERIOUS "MR. JACOBS"

BROOKES, J., *Manners and Customs of the English Nation*. J. Blackwood, London. 1859.

BROWN, A., *The First Republic in America*. Houghton, Mifflin & Co., New York. 1898.

DAWSON, T., *Kemys, Lawrence. A Relation of His Second Voyage to Guiana, South America*. Charles Scribner's Sons, New York. 1912.

FLEISCHLI, J. H., *The St. Bernard Dog* (and Hospice). Judy Publishing Co., Chicago. 1936.

HENRY, W. W., "The Settlement at Jamestown," Virginia Historical Society *Proceedings*, pp. 10-63, Richmond, Va. 1882.

HÜHNER, L., "The Jews of Virginia from the Earliest Times," A. J. H. S. *Publications*, Vol. XX.

MAGNUS, K., *Outlines of Jewish History*. (Edward Nicholas, pp. 249-250.) The Jewish Publication Society of America, Philadelphia. 1890.

OPPENHEIM, S., "A List of Jews Made Denizens in the Reigns of Charles II and James II," A. J. H. S. *Publications*, Vol. XX.

SMITH, J., *A Map of Virginia with Description of the Country*. J. Barnes, Oxford, England. 1612.

SPARKES, M., *The Generall Historie of Virginia by Captaine John Smith*. I. D. and I. H., publishers, London. 1624.

WARNER, G. F., *The Nicholas Papers* (including "An Apology for the Jews"). The Camden Society, London. 1886.

WOLF, L., *Essays in Jewish History* (containing "Cromwell's Jewish Intelligences" and "Crypto-Jews under the Commonwealth"). Jewish History Society of England, London. 1934.

————, *Menasseh ben Israel's Mission to Oliver Cromwell*. Macmillan & Co., London, 1901.

ADVENTURES OF JACOB BARSIMSON

BRÓDY, SÁNDOR, *Rembrandt* (translated by Louis Rittenberg). Globus Press, New York. 1928.

DALY, C. P., *The Settlement of the Jews in North America*. P. Cowen, New York. 1893.

Encyclopædia Britannica. Article: "Menasseh ben Israel."

Encyclopædia Britannica. Article: "Montaigne."

FERNOW, B., *The Records of New Amsterdam*. Knickerbocker Press, New York. 1897.

The Ha-Measeph German-Jewish magazine. Holland. 1784.

INNES, J. H., *New Amsterdam and Its People*. Charles Scribner's Sons, New York. 1902.

KOHLER, M. J., "Beginnings of New York Jewish History," A. J. H. S. *Publications*, Vol. I.

New York Genealogical Records, Vol. XIV. Albany, N. Y.

TODD, C. B., *Story of the City of New York*. G. P. Putnam's Sons, New York. 1888.

VALENTINE, D. T., *History of the City of New York*. G. P. Putnam's Sons, New York. 1853.

WATSON, J. F., *Annals of New York City*. H. F. Anners, Philadelphia. 1846.

DAVID, THE PEDDLER

"Excelsior" *History of the United States*. W. H. Sadlier, New York. 1905.

FRIEDENBERG, A. M., "The Jews of New Jersey from the Earliest Times," A. J. H. S. *Publications*, Vol. XVII.

HÜHNER, L., "The Jews of New England," A. J. H. S. *Publications*, Vol. XI.

KAYSERLING, M., "The Colonization of America by the Jews," A. J. H. S. *Publications*, Vol. II.

MACAULEY, T. B., *History of England*. Longmans, Green & Co., London. 1897.

STRAUS, O. S., *Roger Williams*. Century Co., New York. 1894.

TRUMBULL, J. H., *Public Records of Connecticut.* Case, Lockwood & Brainwood Co., Hartford, Conn. 1850.

WEEDEN, W. B., *Three Commonwealths—Massachusetts, Connecticut and Rhode Island.* C. Hamilton, Worcester, Mass. 1903.

A JEW AMONG THE QUAKERS

DEUTSCH, G., *History of the Jews.* Bloch Publishing Co., New York. 1910.

DUNLOP, O. J., *History of English Apprenticeship and Child Labor,* p. 139, footnote. T. F. Unwin, London. 1912.

FISHER, S. G., *Pennsylvania, Colony and Commonwealth.* H. T. Coates & Co., Philadelphia. 1847.

————, *William Penn,* p. 230, (Penn takes possession of his colony). J. B. Lippincott Co., Philadelphia. 1900.

INNES, T., *The Life of King James II.* Longmans & Co., London. 1816.

MORAIS, H. S., *The Jews of Philadelphia.* The Levytype Co., Philadelphia. 1894.

PHILIPSON, D., *Old European Jewries.* The Jewish Publication Society of America, Philadelphia. 1894.

Proud's History of Pennsylvania, pp. 252-260 (William Penn's descriptive letter of Pennsylvania). Z. Poulson, Philadelphia. 1797.

THORNBURY, W., *Old and New London.* Cassell & Co., London. 1887.

WATSON, J. F., *Annals of Philadelphia.* G. C. & H. Carvill, New York. 1830.

WHEATLEY, H. B., *Samuel Pepys' Diary—and the World He Lived In.* (Filthy and plague-infested condition of London at that period.) Scribner and Welford, New York. 1880.

FROM DEBTORS' PRISON

DEUTSCH, G., *History of the Jews,* p. 91. Bloch Publishing Co., New York. 1910.

DICKENS, C., *Pickwick Papers.* (Description of London's

Debtors' Prison.) Charles Scribner's Sons, New York. 1909.

HOOLE, E., *Oglethorpe and the Wesleys in America*. R. Needham, London. 1863.

HÜHNER, L., "Jewish Women in America." Pamphlet reprinted from *The American Hebrew* magazine. 1918, pp. 6 and 7.

JONES, C. J., JR., "The Settlement of the Jews in Georgia," A. J. H. S. *Publications*, Vol. I.

KAYSERLING, M., "The Colonization of America by the Jews," A. J. H. S. *Publications*, Vol. II.

MARKENS, I., *The Hebrews in America*. (List of names of first Jewish colonists, under chapter head "Savannah," pp. 45-52.) Privately printed, New York. 1888.

OGLETHORPE, J. E., *An Impartial Account* (of Georgia Settlement). J. Hugginson, London. 1742.

————, "Letters from General Oglethorpe," Georgia Historical Society's *Collections*, Vol. III, pp. 1-156. Savannah, Ga.

PETERS, M. C., *Justice to the Jew*. Pp. 42, 43. F. T. Neely, New York. 1899.

WESLEY, J., *An Extract of the Rev. Mr. John Wesley's Journal*. (From his embarking for Georgia to his return to London.) R. Hawes, London. 1775.

————, *The Journal of the Rev. John Wesley*. Eaton & Mains, New York. 1909.

THE CLAN RIDES TONIGHT

FISHER, S. G., *William Penn*. J. B. Lippincott Co., Philadelphia. 1900.

JENKINS, H. M., *The Family of William Penn*. Hadley Bros., London. 1899.

MARKENS, I., *The Hebrews in America*. Chap. "Lancaster, Pa.," pp. 78-83. Privately printed, New York. 1888.

MYERS, A. C., *Narratives of Early Pennsylvania*. Jewish Publication Society of America, Philadelphia. 1894.

NECARSULMER, H., "The Early Jewish Settlement at Lancaster, Pa." A. J. H. S. *Publications*, Vol. IX.

WIERNIK, P., *History of the Jews in America*. Jewish Press Publishing Co., Philadelphia. 1931.

THROUGH THE VALLEY OF TRIBULATION

Encyclopædia Britannica. Article: "Daniel Boone" (Braddock's Expedition).

EZEKIEL, H. T., "Jews in the Southern Colonies," *The American Hebrew* magazine, September 30, 1921, pp. 484, 523.

MADDEN, J., "Braddock's Expedition." Privately printed pamphlet.

SPARKS, J., *Life of George Washington*. Tappan & Dennet, Boston. 1842.

THACKERAY, W. M., *The Virginians*. (The ninth chapter gives a description of Braddock's expedition.) Harper & Brothers, New York. 1859.

TONER, J. M., *Journal of Colonel George Washington*. J. Munsell's Sons, Albany, N. Y. 1893.

West Virginia Historical Magazine, Vol. II, No. 3, pp. 16-36. (Braddock's expedition.)

WOLF, S., *The American Jew as Patriot, Soldier and Citizen*, p. 44. The Levytype Co., Philadelphia. 1895.

THE YELLOW TOPAZ

CARLYLE, T., *Carlyle's Complete Works* (People's Edition). Vol. V. "History of Frederick II, called the Great," (account of Duchy of Mecklenburg). Estes & Lauriat, Boston. 1885.

DEUTSCH, G., *History of the Jews*. Bloch Publishing Co., New York. 1910.

ELZAS, B. A., *The Jews of South Carolina*. (Chapter on "Moses Lindo and the Salvadors.") The Daggett Printing Co., Charleston, S. C. 1903.

HÜHNER, L., "The Jews of South Carolina," A. J. H. S. *Publications*, Vol. XII.

Jewish Encyclopedia. Headings: "South Carolina" and "Lindo" refer to the great topaz.

PETERS, M. C., *Justice to the Jew.* (English Jewish scientists— the Herschels, astronomers, and others.) T. F. Neely, New York. 1899.

Scribners' Narratives of Early Carolina. Charles Scribner's Sons, New York. 1922.

THE *Pride of Newport*

ABBOTT, W. J., *The Story of Our Merchant Marine.* Dodd, Mead & Co., New York. 1919.

American Antiquarian Society's *Proceedings,* XVIII, 106-117. Worcester, Mass.

CAHOONE, S. S., *Sketches of Newport.* J. S. Taylor & Co., New York. 1842.

DANIELS, A. J., *History of the Jews of Boston and New England.* Boston. 1892.

HÜHNER, L., "Jewish Women in America." Pamphlet reprinted from *The American Hebrew* magazine. 1918.

JACOBS, J., *Jewish Contributions to Civilization.* The Jewish Publication Society of America, Philadelphia. 1919.

KOHLER, M. J., "Jewish Activity in American Colonial Commerce," A. J. H. S. *Publications,* Vol. X.

————, "The Jews in Newport," A. J. H. S. *Publications,* Vol. VI.

MARKENS, I., *The Hebrews in America.* (Chap. "Newport," pp. 33-45.) Privately printed, New York. 1888.

WEEDEN, W. B., *Three Commonwealths.* Press of C. Hamilton, Worcester, Mass. 1903.

IN THE DAYS OF THE REGULATORS

BANCROFT, G., *History of the United States,* Vol. VI. Little, Brown & Co., Boston. 1841.

COTTON, E. R., *Life of Hon. Nathaniel Macon.* Lucas & Deaver, Baltimore. 1840.

EZEKIEL, H. T., "Jews in the Southern Colonies." *The American Hebrew* magazine, September 30, 1921, pp. 484, 523.

Haywood, M. D., *Governor William Tryon*. E. M. Uzzell, Raleigh, N. C. 1903.

Hühner, L., "The Struggle for Religious Liberty in North Carolina," A. J. H. S. *Publications*, Vol. XVI.

Madden, L., *The Harmons in the Revolution*. W. M. Clemens, New York. 1913.

Scribners' Narratives of Early Carolina. Charles Scribner's Sons, New York. 1922.

Tappan, E. M., *United States History*. Houghton, Mifflin Co., Boston. 1914.

The Jew Who Would Not Fight

Greene, G. W., *Life of General Nathaniel Greene*. Little, Brown & Co., Boston. 1846.

Jewish Encyclopedia. Article: "New Hampshire."

Runnels, M. T., *History of Sanbornton*. A. Mudge & Son, Boston. 1881.

They Made a Covenant

Bancroft, G., *History of the United States*. Little, Brown & Co., Boston. 1841.

Encyclopædia Britannica. Article: "La Fayette," Vol. XVI. (Lafayette's escape in disguise and his defiant departure from Bordeaux, France, "with eleven chosen companions" to aid America.)

Encyclopædia Britannica. Article: "Michel de Montaigne" (his Jewish ancestry).

Jewish Encyclopedia. Article: "Bordeaux, France," XVIII, 748.

Leavenworth, P., "The Jews and the Wars of America." *The American Hebrew* magazine, September 30, 1921, pp. 486, 522.

Levinger, L. J., *A History of the Jews in the United States*. (Page 117: "the Jews' company.") Union of American Hebrew Congregations, Cincinnati. 1931.

Markens, I., *The Hebrews in America*. Privately printed, New York. 1888.

LIST OF REFERENCES

WOLF, S., *The American Jew as Patriot, Soldier and Citizen,* pp. 44-52, 547, 548. The Levytype Co., Philadelphia. 1895.

THE KING'S DIAMOND

The Dearborn Independent, "Aspects of Jewish Power in the United States." Dearborn Publishing Company, Dearborn, Mich. 1922.

DENNY, E., *Military Journal of Major E. Denny.* Pennsylvania Historical Society *Memoirs,* VII, 205-492, Philadelphia, 1860.

Encyclopædia Britannica. Article: "Lord Chamberlain." (Office of the royal jewels.) XVII, 1. Article: "George III." (Mental breakdown of the King.) XI, 742.

England's National Register, for 1761, p. 234. London, England.

HUGHES, T. S., *History of England,* I, 238. G. Bell, London. 1846.

JESSE, J. H., *Memoirs of King George III,* I, 110. Tinsley Bros., London. 1867.

JONES, W., *Crowns and Coronations,* p. 322. Chatto & Winders, London. 1902.

KEMBLE, S., *The Kemble Papers,* I, 28. New York Historical Society, New York. 1884. (Description of a ball at the Franks' family home near London.)

KOHLER, M. J., "Haym Salomon" pamphlet. Privately printed, New York. 1931.

MARKENS, I., *The Hebrews in America,* p. 66. (The deep friendship of the Hanover Georges and the Franks family.) Privately printed, New York. 1888.

Numerous papers on the Franks family and connection with Haym Salomon, A. J. H. S. *Publications,* Vols. I, V, X, XXV.

PASSINGHAM, W. J., *History of the Coronation* (George III), p. 231. S. Low, Marston & Co., London. 1937.

The Remembrancer or Impartial Repository of Public Events, pp. 100-106. Magazine published in London, England. 1776. (David S. Franks' adventures in Montreal, Canada.)

Sparks, J., *Diplomatic Correspondence of the United States Government*, II, 382. N. Hale, Gray & Bowen, New York. 1829. (Major D. S. Franks as emissary to Europe.)

Van Schaak, P., *The Life of Peter Van Schaak* (an American exile in England), p. 143. D. Appleton & Co., New York. 1842. (Descriptive of the Franks' London home.)

Wolf, S., *The American Jew as Patriot, Soldier and Citizen*. Article: "Colonel David S. Franks," pp. 27-32, by M. J. Kohler. The Levytype Co., Philadelphia. 1895.

Wright, T., *England Under the Hanovers*, I, 393. R. Bentley, London. 1848. (The great Coronation diamond falls.)

Levy, the Lion-Hearted

Ree, Mrs. Virginia (née Lopez), widow of Commodore Uriah P. Levy, "Reminiscences" presented by B. W. Blandford in *The American Hebrew* magazine, April 10 to May 15, 1925.

Roosevelt, Theodore, *The Naval War of 1812*. G. P. Putnam's Sons, New York. 1882.

United States Army and Navy Magazine, August, 1893.

Aaron Wolf, Young Hero of Texas

Cohen, H., "The Settlement of the Jews in Texas," A. J. H. S. *Publications*, Vols. II and IV.

Powell, E. A., *Some Forgotten Heroes*. Charles Scribner's Sons, New York. 1922.

Wolf, S., *The American Jew as Patriot, Soldier and Citizen*, pp. 72-83. (A. Wolf, killed at the storming of the Alamo; Adolphus Sterne, Dr. Levy, Captain Harby, and other Jews.) The Levytype Co., Philadelphia. 1895.

A Million Pounds Sterling

Chittenden, L. E., *Recollections of President Lincoln and His Administration*, Chap. XXV, pp. 197-203. (This is also included in S. Wolf's book, pp. 91-97.) Harper & Brothers, New York. 1891.

ROUTH, H. V., *England Under Victoria*. Methuen & Co., London. 1930.

WOLF, S., *The American Jew as Patriot, Soldier and Citizen.* "A Page from the Secret History of the Civil War," pp. 87-90. ("the man was a Jew"—p. 89.) The Levytype Co.. Philadelphia. 1895.

THE PRIMROSE LEAGUE

DEWEY, G., *Autobiography of Admiral George Dewey*, pp. 253-264. (Incident of German warship *Irene*.) Charles Scribner's Sons, New York. 1916.

Encyclopædia Britannica. Articles: "Spain," "Cuba," "Spanish-American War," "Sir Joseph Wolff Drummond," etc.

MONYPENNY, W. F., *The Life of Benjamin Disraeli*, II, 1500-1503. (The Primrose League, formed in London in 1883, received its name from the honored Jew's favorite flower, the common wild primrose, a symbol of simple loyalty.) Macmillan Co., New York, 1929.

SICKEL, W., *Disraeli, A Study in Personality and Ideas*. Methuen & Co., London. 1904.

WILCOX, M., *History of the War with Spain*. Frederick A. Stokes Co., New York. 1898.

UNION GRADED SERIES

EDITED BY

EMANUEL GAMORAN, PH.D., *Director of Education*
Union of American Hebrew Congregations